THE
JAPANESE ABACUS
EXPLAINED

by

Y. YOSHINO

with an introduction by
MARTIN GARDNER

Dover Publications, Inc.

New York

Published in Canada by General Publishing Company, Ltd., 30 Lesmill Road, Don Mills, Toronto, Ontario.

Published in the United Kingdom by Constable and Company, Ltd., 10 Orange Street, London W. C. 2.

Q A
75
. Y 6
1963
(1)

This Dover edition, first published in 1963, is an unabridged and unaltered republication of the work first published by Kyo Bun Kwan, Tokyo, in 1937.

This volume also contains a new Introduction by Martin Gardner especially prepared for this Dover edition.

Library of Congress Catalog Card Number: 63-20256

Manufactured in the United States of America

Dover Publications, Inc.
180 Varick Street
New York 14, N. Y.

Introduction to Dover Edition

Why should anyone in the western world, in this day of versatile office calculating machines and mammoth electronic computers, waste his time learning how to use a simple abacus? There are several reasons.

In the first place, the office calculators are expensive. Who wants to spend a hundred dollars or more on a computer to use, outside a business office, on those rare occasions when a long list of numbers has to be added? The abacus, in contrast, is ideal for home use or by a small shopkeeper. It costs little, operates reliably, requires no maintenance, can be carried in the coat pocket, and makes an unusual pattern hanging on a wall.

In the second place, using an abacus is *more fun* than adding or subtracting on paper. For many years, ever since I was introduced to the abacus by a friend, L. Vosburgh Lyons, I have used it for adding figures in check books, totaling store receipts, and on countless other occasions when a tedious numerical calculation presented itself. The tactile sensation of clicking the beads back and forth turns a dull task into a pleasant one. The mind has less work to do than when figuring with pencil and paper, and there is a pleasure in developing the finger skills that make for rapid manipulation of the beads.

In the third place, working with the abacus introduces one to an interesting segment of eastern culture. Not only is the abacus still widely used throughout Japan, China and India, but in the Soviet Union as well. If you buy more than one item in any Moscow store the chances are ten to one that the storekeeper will tally up the prices on an abacus. Learning to use the device is something like developing a taste for Japanese *sukiyaki* or Russian *kvas*. It helps in its small way to bridge cultural gaps. Lyons once told me that he was in a Chinese laundry one day where he overheard a surly gentleman demanding to know how much he owed. "Hurry up and figure it out," the man said, "on that crazy thing there of yours." The remark is typical of a barbarian in a minor state of what anthropologists call "cultural shock." Anything alien to his own experience is inferior, childish, a bit "crazy."

Finally, there is (at least for me) a pleasure in rebelling against the enormous overcomplexity of modern life. "Simplicity, simplicity, simplicity!" cried Henry David Thoreau. "I say, let your affairs be as two or three, and not a hundred or a thousand; instead of a million count half a dozen, and keep your accounts on your thumb nail." The abacus could hardly be simpler; yet it does exactly what it is supposed to do, with great efficiency, without electrical switches, vacuum tubes, transistors; without even a single lever or cogwheel. Discovering it is like a modern housewife's discovery that an excellent clothes dryer can be made from a piece of rope stretched horizontally. On the wall, near a giant computer, one sometimes sees an abacus behind glass, with the sign: IN CASE OF EMERGENCY, USE THIS. I for one take a perverse delight in operating a digital computer so simple that even the ancient Romans were able to manufacture it.

A skilled abacus operator can hold his own with a skilled machine operator, except on large problems of multiplication and division. Whenever a contest in speed and accuracy is staged between an abacus and a modern desk calculator, the abacus usually wins. In 1946, wide publicity was given to a contest in Tokyo (on November 11 in the Ernie Pyle Theater) between Private Thomas Nathan Wood, of Deering, Missouri, using an American office machine, and Kiyoshi Matsuzaki, a local abacus expert. Private Wood was not a skilled operator, so perhaps the contest was a bit rigged*; nevertheless, the audience was astounded when Matsuzaki won. A week later a similar contest was staged in New York for broadcast over radio station WOR. A huge office machine was wheeled into the studio on a typewriter table, for operation by Dorothy Boudreau of the WOR payroll department. Mr. P. T. So, a Chinese student at Columbia University, took his wooden abacus out of his brief case. Mr. So, who later apologized for being so clumsy, finished eight seconds ahead of his opponent.

The Chinese abacus or *suan-pan,* by the way, is a bit different from the Japanese *soroban.* It has an extra row of beads on top, another extra row on the bottom. Both rows are little used in ordinary computation, and since the nineteenth century have been dropped entirely from the modern *soroban.* However, if you happen to own a Chinese abacus instead of a Japanese model, there is no need to discard it. Everything in this clearly written, elementary manual is applicable; just ignore the top and bottom rows of beads.

For practice in addition, let me recommend the following amusing exercise. Place on the abacus the number 12345679 (note omission of the 8). Add this number to itself eight times, which is the same as multiplying it by 9. The result will be a sum consisting entirely of 1's. Add 12345679 nine more times to get a row of 2's. Nine more times produces a row of 3's, and so on until you have added the number 80 times to finish with 999,999,999. It is a good exercise because it exploits every variety of bead manipulation, and in a series of stages that are easy to check. By timing yourself each time you com-

---

* See the letter by Major A. M. Maish in *Mathematics Magazine,* Vol. 29, No. 1, September-October, 1955, giving details of the contest not covered in the wire service accounts.

plete a stage correctly you can see how your speed is improving. An expert can do each stage of nine additions in half a minute.
  Happy bead flicking!

Dobbs Ferry, N. Y.   MARTIN GARDNER
July, 1963

FOREWORD

The following pages have been written for High School and College students, either boys or girls, and for anyone who may be interested in a study of the abacus.

The author, when he voyaged to the United States some years ago, found many friends there who wanted to know about the abacus or Japanese *soroban*. It was understood that the abacus had educational value, not to mention its usefulness, but they could not find an account of it in any of the textbooks in use.

In the pages that follow, methods of calculation on the abacus, in use in Japan from ancient times to the present, are described.

The abacus is more accurate and a quicker instrument of calculation than the use of figures written down. In size and cost of production, it is more convenient and less expensive than calculating machines.

For this reason, the abacus is recognized in commercial circles in Japan as the best instrument for making all calculations.

This book has been written in simple and plain English, with numerous illustrations or diagrams, in order to make the subject as clear as possible to the reader. It should be borne in mind that the abacus is used with almost incredible speed in making calculations. It is also not to be overlooked that a mental process accompanies the manipulation of the counters with the fingers.

The author hopes that all his American friends will be helped, by the use of this treatise, to understand and use the abacus, and that they may be able to acquire the speed and accuracy achieved in every day life here in Japan. If so, the author's purpose in writing this book will have been fulfilled.

Y. Yoshino, author
Kuragano, Japan
February 15, 1937

CONTENTS

CHAPTER I.

ABACUS

Section 1.

The names of the parts of an abacus.

A is the crosspiece
B is an upright
C is the upper part or Heaven
D is the lower part or Earth

The crosspiece divides the abacus into two compartments. The upper one is called "Heaven" and the lower one "Earth."

An upright serves as an axis for the counters.

The counters in "Heaven" are generally worth five points while those in "Earth" are worth only one. Before beginning to use the abacus all the Heaven counters must be pushed up to the top of their uprights. This can be done with one sweeping movement of the fingers.

The uprights on the left hand side form the "upper position" and those on the right the "lower position."

For example, if we wish to show the number 152 on the abacus we must begin from the left as is shown in the following illustration.

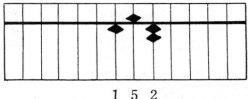

1 5 2

In this case the first upright stands for one hundreds, the second for tens, and the third for ones. Therefore we need one one-hundreds, five tens, and two ones.

Section 2.

The value of the counters.

A counter in Heaven is worth 5.

A counter in Earth is worth 1.

Therefore one counter in Heaven is worth five counters in Earth and is generally spoken of as the 5 counter.

Section 3.

How to place and to return the counters.

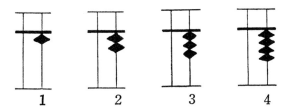

| 1 | 2 | 3 | 4 |

To designate the numbers 1, 2, 3, and 4 the Earth counters are used.

 5

To designate 5 a counter of Heaven is used.

 6

To designate 6 a counter of Heaven and one of Earth are used.

 7

To designate 7 a counter of Heaven and two of Earth are used.

8   To designate 8 one counter of Heaven and three of Earth are used.

 9   To designate 9 one counter of Heaven and four of Earth are used.

As the above illustrations show when we use the counters for numbers less than 5 we lift into place the Earth counters beginning with the top one. When the number is larger than 5 we push down into place one of the Heaven counters and then lift up the Earth counters as needed.

As for example the following illustration shows the numbers 5, 7, and 12 in position.

5 and 7 are 12.

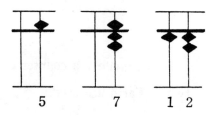

5   7   1   2

4

If the number 5 is indicated on the abacus and we wish to add to it the number 7, we must raise into position two Earth counters on the same upright as the 5 and at the same time push back into place the 5 counter and raise one Earth counter on the next upright to the left. Thus we see that the sum is 12.

The uprights on the left are always of higher value than those on the right so if we raise one earth counter on each of three uprights in succession from left to right we get the number one hundred and twenty three.

Upper side   Lower side

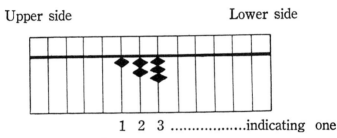

1 2 3 ....indicating one hundred and twenty three.

Section 4.

The Proper Use of the Fingers.

In handling the counters we should use two fingers, the thumb and forefinger.

The forefinger should be used to place into position the 5 counters and to return to place the Earth counters after using, and sometimes to return to place the Heaven counters.

The thumb should be used to raise into position the Earth counters and sometimes to return to place the 5 counters.

Care should be taken to train the thumb and the forefinger to perform these duties.

I should like to mention some other things about using the abacus.

(1) Keep a good posture, bending forward a little.

(2) Hold the back of the abacus in your left palm and do not lay your right hand on your desk as it must be kept free to move any counter on the board.

(3) When using the abacus clinch your right hand together with the exception of the thumb and forefinger.

(4) Do not spread your fingers.

(5) You must train yourself to recognize the figures as quickly as possible and accurately.

(6) You must recognize figures instantly and in proportion to your progress learn to recognize two or three figures at a time.

CHAPTER II.

ADDITION

Addition is the summing up of two or more figures.

Section 1.

Addition Table.

Memorize the following table.

$1 + 9 = 10$	One	and	Nine	are	Ten.
$2 + 8 = 10$	Two	and	Eight	are	Ten.
$3 + 7 = 10$	Three	and	Seven	are	Ten.
$4 + 6 = 10$	Four	and	Six	are	Ten.
$5 + 5 = 10$	Five	and	Five	are	Ten.
$6 + 4 = 10$	Six	and	Four	are	Ten.
$7 + 3 = 10$	Seven	and	Three	are	Ten.
$8 + 2 = 10$	Eight	and	Two	are	Ten.
$9 + 1 = 10$	Nine	and	One	are	Ten.

Section 2.

Practical use of the counters in addition.

From the explanations in the preceding chapters addition should be clear by now but as it is necessary to understand well in the beginning let me show you a practical addition in the following problem.

Find the sum of 5 and 1.

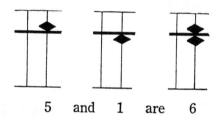

5   and   1   are   6

The use of the fingers :

With the forefinger, slide down the 5 counter first.

With the thumb, lift up the 1 counter on the same upright.

The sum is indicated as 6. ·

A few examples will give you practical training which will help you to understand. In these exercises the abbreviation " A. T." means " Addition Table."

Part One.

Adding with numbers of one place.

Example 1. 5 and 1 are 6.

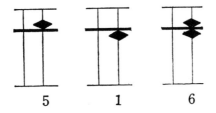

5   1   6

(1) Slide down a 5 counter with the forefinger.

(2) Raise a 1 counter on the same upright with the thumb.

The sum 6 is indicated on the board.

Example 2. 5 and 2 are 7.

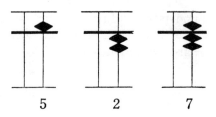

(1) Slide down a 5 counter with the forefinger.

(2) Raise two of the Earth counters on the same **upright,** with the thumb.

The sum 7 is indicated on the board.

Example 3. 5 and 3 are 8.

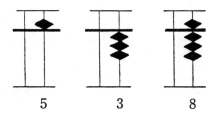

(1) Slide down a 5 counter with the forefinger.

(2) Raise three of the earth counters on the same **upright,** with the thumb.

The sum 8 is indicated on the board.

10

Example 4. 5 and 4 are 9.

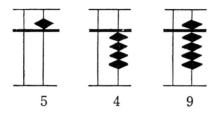

5   4   9

(1) Slide down one of the Heaven counters with the forefinger.

(2) Raise four of the Earth counters which are on the same upright as the Heaven counter, using the thumb.

The sum 9 is indicated on the board.

Example 5. 1 and 5 are 6.

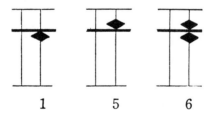

1   5   6

(1) Raise one Earth counter with the thumb.

(2) Slide down a Heaven counter on the same upright, with the forefinger.

The sum 6 is indicated on the board.

11

Example 6. 2 and 5 are 7.

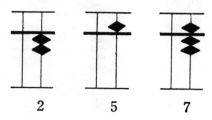

2   5   7

(1)   With the thumb raise two Earth counters.

(2)   With the forefinger slide down one Heaven counter on the same upright as the two 1 counters.

The sum 7 is indicated on the board.

Example 7. 3 and 5 are 8.

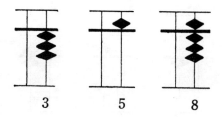

3   5   8

(1)   With the thumb lift into place three of the 1 counters.

(2)   With the forefinger slide down one of the 5 counters on the same upright as the three 1 counters.

The sum 8 is indicated on the board.

12

Example 8. 4 and 5 are 9.

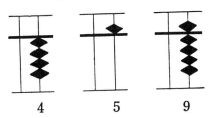

(1) With the thumb raise into position four of the one counters.

(2) With the forefinger slide down into position the 5 counter on the same upright as the four one counters.

The sum 9 is indicated on the board.

Example 9. 6 and 1 are 7.

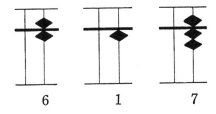

(1) With one movement press down a 5 counter and slide up a one counter, the forefinger on the Heaven counter and the thumb on the Earth one.

(2) With the thumb raise one Earth counter on the same upright with the other two. The sum 7 is indicated on the board.

Example 10. 6 and 3 are 9.

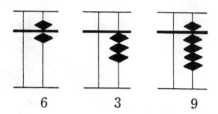

(1) As before with one movement press down a 5 counter and shove up a 1 counter with the forefinger and the thumb.

(2) With the thumb raise three of the one counters on the same upright with the other two.

The sum 9 is indicated on the board.

Example 11. 2 and 7 are 9.

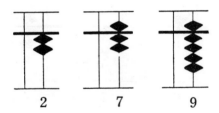

(1) With the thumb raise two Earth counters.

(2) With one movement raise two Earth counters with the thumb and one Heaven counter with the forefinger, on the same upright with the two Earth counters. Thus one Heaven counter and four Earth counters in position indicate the sum 9.

14

Example 12. 3 and 6 are 9.

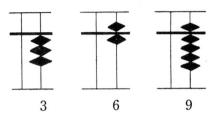

      3   6   9

(1) Raise three Earth counters with the thumb.

(2) With one movement push down one Heaven counter with the forefinger and push up one Earth counter on the same upright with the thumb.

9 is indicated on the board. This is the sum.

Example 13. 1 and 4 are 5.

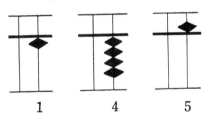

      1   4   5

(1) With the thumb raise one Earth counter.

(2) Think "1 and 4 are 5." With the forefinger take down one of the five counters on the same upright as the one Earth counter and at the same time replace the one counter which was moved into position.

The sum 5 is indicated on the board.

Example 14. 2 and 4 are 6.

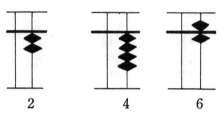

(1) With the thumb raise two Earth counters.

(2) Think, "4 and 1 are 5." With the forefinger slide down the Heaven counter on the same upright as the two Earth counters and return one of the Earth counters to its original position.

The sum 6 is indicated on the board.

Example 15. 3 and 4 are 7.

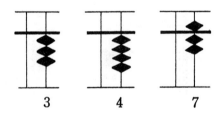

(1) With the thumb raise three Earth counters.

(2) Think, "4 and 1 are 5." Take down the Heaven counter on the same upright as the three Earth counters and at the same time with the same forefinger replace one of the Earth counters.

The sum 7 is indicated on the board.

16

Example 16. 4 and 4 are 8.

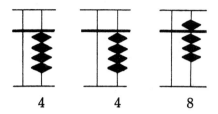

(1) With the thumb raise four of the one counters.

(2) Think, "4 and 1 are 5." Slide down the Heaven counter on the same upright with the four Earth counters and at the same time replace one of the Earth counters with the forefinger.

The sum 8 is indicated on the board.

Example 17. 4 and 3 are 7.

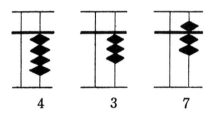

(1) With the thumb raise four Earth counters.

(2) Think, "3 and 2 are 5." With the forefinger slide down the Heaven counter on the same upright as the four Earth counters and replace 2 of the Earth counters.

The sum 7 is indicated on the board.

17

Example 18. 3 and 3 are 6.

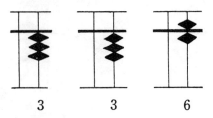

(1) With the thumb raise three Earth counters.

(2) Think "3 and 2 are 5." Slide down the Heaven counter on the same upright as the three Earth counters and at the same time with the forefinger replace 2 of the Earth counters.

The sum 6 is indicated on the board.

Example 19. 2 and 3 are 5.

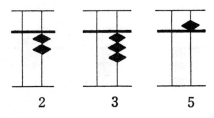

(1) With the thumb raise two of the Earth counters.

(2) Think, "2 and 3 are 5" and with the forefinger slide down the 5 counter on the same upright as the two Earth counters. At the same time return to place the two Earth counters.

The sum 5 is indicated on the board.

18

Example 20. 4 and 2 are 6.

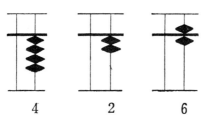

4   2   6

(1) With the thumb raise four of the one counters.

(2) Think, "2 and 3 are 5." With the forefinger take down the 5 counter on the same upright with the four one counters and at the same time replace three of the one counters.

The sum 6 is indicated on the board.

Example 21. 3 and 2 are 5.

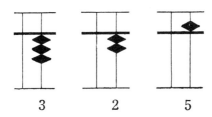

3   2   5

(1) With the thumb raise three of the one counters into place.

(2) Think, "2 and 3 are 5." With the forefinger slide down the 5 counter on the same upright and at the same time return to their original position the three one counters.

The sum 5 is indicated on the board.

19

Example 22. 4 and 1 are 5.

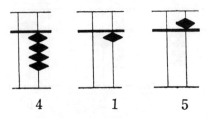

(1) With the thumb raise four of the one counters.

(2) Think, "1 and 4 are 5." With the forefinger take down the 5 counter on the same upright as the four counters and at the same time return the four counters to place.

The sum 5 is indicated on the board.

Example 23. 1 and 9 are 10.

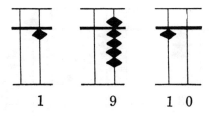

(1) With the thumb raise one Earth counter.

(2) Think, "A. T. 1 and 9 are 10." With the forefinger replace the one counter and at the same time with the thumb raise one of the Earth counters on the next upright to the left.

The sum 10 is indicated on the board.

Example 24. 2 and 8 are 10.

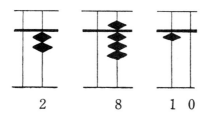

2   8   1 0

(1) With the thumb raise two of the Earth counters.

(2) Think, "A. T. 2 and 8 are 10." With the forefinger replace the two Earth counters and at the same time raise one of the Earth counters on the next upright to the left, with the thumb.

The sum 10 is indicated on the board.

Example 25. 3 and 7 are 10.

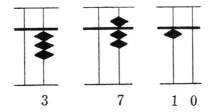

3   7   1 0

(1) With the thumb raise three of the Earth counters.

(2) Think, "A. T. 3 and 7 are 10." With the forefinger return the three Earth counters and at the same time raise one of the Earth counters on the next upright to the left, with the thumb.

The sum 10 is indicated on the board.

21

Example 26. 4 and 6 are 10.

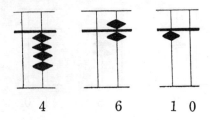

4   6 1 0

(1) With the thumb raise four Earth counters.

(2) Think, "A. T. 4 and 6 are 10." At one time replace the four Earth counters with the forefinger and raise one Earth counter on the next upright to the left, with the thumb.

The sum 10 is indicated.

Example 27. 5 and 5 are 10.

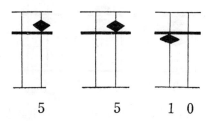

5   5 1 0

(1) With the forefinger slide down a Heaven counter.

(2) Think, "A. T. 5 and 5 are 10." With the forefinger replace the Heaven counter and at the same time raising one Earth counter on the next upright to the left, with the thumb.

The sum 10 is indicated.

22

Example 28. 5 and 6 are 11.

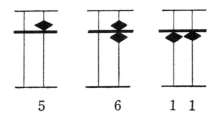

(1) With the forefinger slide down a Heaven counter.

(2) Think, "A. T. 5 and 5 are 10." Raise one Earth counter on the same upright as the Heaven counter which is in position. Do this with the thumb. With one movement return the Heaven counter with the forefinger and with the thumb raise one Earth counter on the next upright to the left.

Eleven is indicated. It is the sum.

Example 29. 5 and 7 are 12.

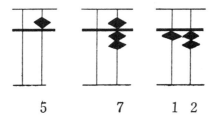

(1) With the forefinger slide down one of the Heaven counters.

(2) Think, "A. T. 5 and 5 are 10." Raise two Earth

counters on the same upright as the Heaven one with the thumb. With the forefinger replace the Heaven counter and with the thumb raise one Earth counter on the next upright to the left.

12 is indicated. It is the sum.

Example 30. 5 and 8 are 13.

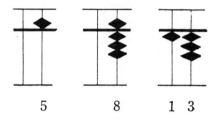

5   8   1 3

(1) With the forefinger slide down a Heaven counter.

(2) Think, " A. T. 5 and 5 are 10." Raise three Earth counters on the same upright as the Heaven counter with the thumb and with the forefinger return the Heaven counter to its place. With the thumb raise one Earth counter on the next upright to the left.

13 is indicated. It is the sum.

Example 31. 6 and 6 are 12.

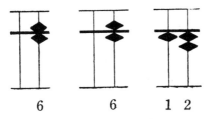

6   6   1   2

(1) With one movement hold between the forefinger and the thumb one Heaven counter and one Earth counter on the same upright. This will indicate 6.

(2) Think, " A. T. 5 and 5 are 10." Raise one Earth counter on the same upright with the other two with the thumb. With the forefinger replace the Heaven counter and at the same time raise one Earth counter on the next upright to the left, with the thumb.

12 is indicated on the board. It is the sum.

Example 32. 7 and 6 are 13.

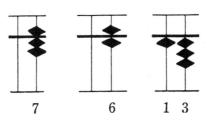

7   6   1   3

(1) Hold between your forefinger and your thumb one Heaven counter and two Earth counters.

25

(2) Think, " A. T. 5 and 5 are 10." Raise one Earth counter on the same upright as those in position, with the thumb. With the forefinger return to its original place the Heaven counter and with the thumb raise one Earth counter on the next upright to the left.

13 is indicated. It is the sum.

Example 33. 8 and 6 are 14.

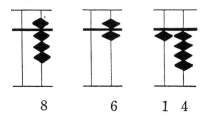

8   6   1 4

(1) Hold between your thumb and forefinger one Heaven counter and three Earth counters on the same upright.

(2) Think, " A. T. 5 and 5 are 10." Raise one Earth counter up with the other two and with the forefinger replace the Heaven counter. With the thumb raise one Earth counter on the next upright to the left.

14 is indicated. It is the sum.

Example 34. 9 and 9 are 18.

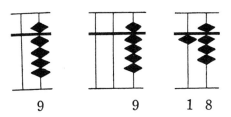

(1) Press between the forefinger and the thumb one Heaven counter and four Earth counters on the same upright.

(2) Think, "A. T. 9 and 1 are 10." Replace one Earth counter which was in position, with the forefinger and at the same time raise one Earth counter on the next upright to the left, with the thumb.

18 is indicated. It is the sum.

Exercise.

Add each column and write the sum.

Row A.	2	3	4	5	7
	3	4	5	6	7

Row B,	8	9	3	5	7
	9	1	5	4	3

Row C.	2	3	6	7	8
	4	6	6	7	8

Row D.	7	3	9	3	2
	8	3	9	9	7

	9	6	5	5	6
	2	8	5	8	8

	4	3	2	1	2
	4	8	7	8	5

When you use the abacus you must constantly think of the Addition Table even though your numbers are small so that you will form a habit which will be helpful when you begin to handle large numbers.

Section 2.

Part 2.

The Determination of the Position on a Board.

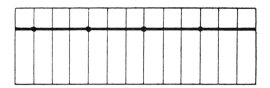

For the sake of convenience the abacus is divided into sections by black spots on the partition between Heaven and Earth.

From one of these black spots one step towards the left is the position for 10's and the next place is for 100's and the next is for 1000's.

For example:

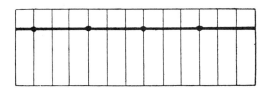

F E D C B A X Y Z

If we decide to use the upright A as the unit position, B is the position for 10's.

C is for 100's
D is for 1000's
E is for 10,000's
F is for 100,000's and so on
X is for one tenth's position
Y is for one hundred's position
Z is for one thousand's position and so on.

The unit position A was chosen in the above example but there is no set rule as to which upright should become the unit upright. Any one which suits your convenience may be chosen, but it should be one with a black spot.

The black spot is very convenient in counting money in the United States. It serves as the decimal point to divide the dollars from the cents.

For example:

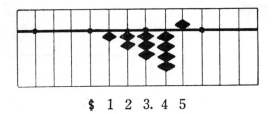

$ 1 2 3. 4 5

The black spot shows that the 123 is dollars and that the 45 is cents.

Section 2.

Part 3.

Illustration of large numbers on a Board.

Now that you understand the determination of a position, chose one upright which is marked by a black dot to serve as the unit position. Then just as in writing a number begin at the left and place the counters into position as needed.

Illustrations will make this point clear.

Example 1.

Designate 112.

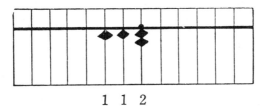

1 1 2

(1) With the thumb raise one Earth counter on the second upright from the one with the black dot. This will indicate one hundred.

(2) With the thumb raise one Earth counter on the first upright to the left. This indicates one ten.

(3) With the thumb raise two Earth counters on the unit upright.

31

This indicates two ones and the whole indicates 112.

Example 2.

Indicate 2,345.

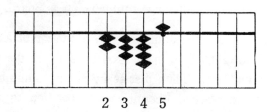

2　3　4　5

(1) With the thumb raise two Earth counters on the third upright to the left of the black spot. This indicates two thousands.

(2) With the thumb raise three Earth counters on the second upright to the left of the unit one. This indicates three one hundreds.

(3) With the thumb raise four counters on the upright on the left of the unit one. This indicates four tens.

(4) With the forefinger slide down the Heaven counter on the unit upright. This indicates five ones.

Altogether 2,345 is indicated.

Section 2.

Part 4.

Adding With Large Numbers.

Adding with numbers of two places or more is the same as adding with numbers less than 10. It is a series of repetition of one place numbers, the only difference being that whenever an upright indicates its full capacity of ten then you must replace all of these counters and raise one Earth counter on the next upright to the left.

Example 1.   56 and 56 are 112.

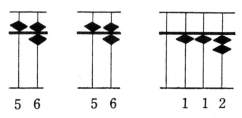

| 5 6 | 5 6 | 1 1 2 |

(1)   With the forefinger slide down one Heaven counter cn the ten upright in relation to the unit counter.

(2)   Press between your fingers the Heaven counter and one Earth counter on the unit upright.

56 is indicated on the board.

(3) Think, " A. T. 5 and 5 are 10." Replace the Heaven counter on the ten upright with the forefinger and at the same time raise one of the Earth counters on the next upright to the left with your thumb. 106 is indicated.

(4) Think, " A. T. 5 and 5 are 10." Raise an Earth counter on the unit upright with the thumb and with the forefinger replace the 5 counter on the same upright. Then raise one Earth counter on the next upright to the left with the thumb.

112 is indicated. It is the sum.

Example 2. 55 and 11 are 66.

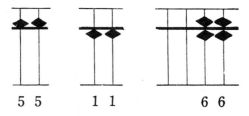

5 5   1 1   6 6

(1) Take down a 5 counter on the ten upright, with the forefinger.

(2) Take down a 5 counter on the unit upright, with the forefinger.

55 is indicated.

(3) Raise one Earth counter on the 10 upright with the thumb.

(4) Raise one Earth counter on the unit upright with the thumb.

66 is indicated on the board. It is the sum.

Example 3. 26 and 42 are 68.

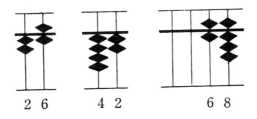

2 6   4 2   6 8

(1) With the thumb raise two Earth counters on the 10 upright.

(2) Press between the forefinger and the thumb the Heaven counter and one Earth counter on the unit upright.

26 is indicated on the board.

(3) Think, "4 and 1 are 5." Slide down the 5 counter on the 10 upright with the forefinger, and at the same time return one Earth counter on the same upright.

(4) Raise two Earth counters on the unit upright with the thumb.

68 is indicated on the board. It is the sum.

Example 4. 33 and 55 are 88.

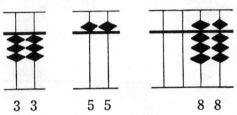

3 3 5 5 8 8

(1) Raise three Earth counters on the 10 position, with the thumb.

(2) Raise three Earth counters on the unit upright, with the thumb.

33 is indicated.

(3) Slide down the 5 counter on the 10 upright with the forefinger.

(4) Slide down the 5 counter on the unit upright with the forefinger.

88 is indicated. It is the sum.

Example 5. 66 and 55 are 121.

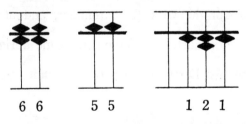

6 6 5 5 1 2 1

(1) Press between the forefinger and the thumb the 5 counter and one Earth counter on the 10 upright.

(2) Hold between the forefinger and the thumb the 5 counter and one Earth counter on the unit upright.

66 is indicated on the board.

(3) Think, "A. T. 5 and 5 are 10." With the forefinger return to position one Heaven counter on the 10 upright, and at the same time raise one Earth counter on the next upright to the left, in this case the 100 position.

116 is indicated on the board.

(4) Think, "A. T. 5 and 5 are 10." With the forefinger replace the Heaven counter on the unit position, and at the same time raise one Earth counter on the next upright to the left, with the thumb.

121 is indicated on the board. It is the sum.

Example 6.   34 and 89 are 123.

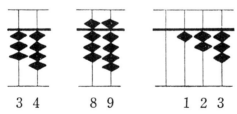

3 4   8 9   1 2 3

(1) Raise three Earth counters on the 10 upright with the thumb.

(2) Raise four Earth counters on the unit upright with the thumb.

34 is indicated on the board.

(3) Think, " A. T. 8 and 2 are 10." With the forefinger return two Earth counters on the 10 upright, and at the same time, with the thumb, raise one Earth counter on the next upright to the left.

114 is indicated on the board.

(4) Think, " A. T. 9 and 1 are 10." With the forefinger return one Earth counter on the unit upright, and at the same time with the thumb, raise one Earth counter on the next upright to the left.

123 is indicated on the board. It is the sum.

Example 7. 333 and 222 are 555.

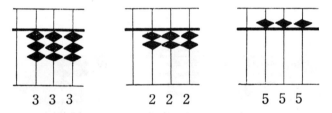

(1) With the thumb raise three Earth counters on the 100 upright.

(2) With the thumb raise three Earth counters on the 10 upright.

(3) With the thumb raise three Earth counters on the unit upright.

333 is indicated on the board.

(4) Think, "2 and 3 are 5." Slide down the Heaven counter on the 100 upright with the forefinger, and at the same time return to place three Earth counters on the same upright.

(5) Think, "2 and 3 are 5." Slide down the Heaven counter on the 10 upright with the forefinger, and at the same time return three Earth counters on the same upright.

(6) Think, "2 and 3 are 5." Slide down the Heaven counter on the unit upright with the forefinger and at the same time return three Earth counters on the same upright.

The sum 555 is indicated on the board.

Example 8. 234 and 999 are 1233.

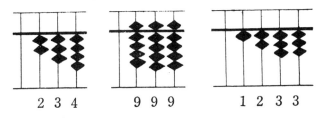

2 3 4   9 9 9   1 2 3 3

(1) With the thumb raise two of the Earth counters on the 100 upright.

(2) With the thumb raise three Earth counters on the 10 upright.

(3) With the thumb raise four Earth counters on the unit upright.

234 is now indicated on the board.

(4) Think, " A. T. 9 and 1 are 10." With the forefinger return one Earth counter on the 100 upright, and at the same time with the thumb raise one Earth counter on the next upright to the left, in this case the 1000 upright.

(5) Think, " A. T. 9 and 1 are 10." With the forefinger return to place one Earth counter on the 10 upright, and at the same time raise one Earth counter on the next upright to the left, with the thumb, in this case the 100 upright.

(6) Think, " A. T. 9 and 1 are 10." With the forefinger return to place one Earth counter on the unit upright, and at the same time with the thumb, raise one Earth counter on the next upright to the left, in this case the 10 upright.

1233 is indicated on the board. It is the sum.

As is shown in the above examples if we remember how to add small numbers on the abacus, and remember the Addition Table we can add numbers of any size.

It is usually more important to do things well than to do them quickly but speed is useful and it will prove worth while to learn to handle the abacus quickly and with accuracy.

It is also useful to know how quickly you can do things and still do them well so time yourself when taking tests, not only in addition but in multiplication as well.

Exercise.

Add and write the sum.

Row A.	22	66	78	56	45
	88	11	21	43	66

Row B.	11	33	33	567	3984
	99	99	88	128	8697

Row C.	22	77	11	11	77
	66	11	22	44	67

Row D.	66	99	64	44	133
	66	22	64	77	345

Adding large numbers is just as simple as the work which you have just been doing.

Row E.

1465	2564	6315	79	91235
8871	1121	572	452	3492
3296	980	1805	4597	515

Row F.

$50.00	$41.93	$15.14	$53.98
6.71	7.76	19.62	4.72
13.25	11.32	31.58	12.63
31.82	90.11	44.33	25.56

Row G.

28	717	42	57	210
191	238	96	41	551
612	112	123	220	75
233	98	19	309	193
425	216	432	167	61
77	9	111	413	250
339	341	302	700	170

As I have said before, it is not enough to understand the method only, you must acquire speed. You must strive towards what we call " a quick addition."

Section 3.

Addition from Dictation.

The success of adding on the abacus while someone dictates is dependent upon the manner in which the numbers are read out.

The following things should be kept in mind by the reader.

(1) Speak clearly and quickly but in a sing-song manner.

(2) Use some connecting word such as "and" or "next" between the numbers.

(3) If great speed is needed the connecting word should be omitted.

(4) Before reading a column of figures give some warning such as, " Ready ? "

(5) If you make a mistake in reading a number ask the adder to add or subtract the amount necessary to correct the mistake. Or if you are worried for fear some mistake has been made ask to begin all over again.

(6) At the end use some expression which signifies that the work is finished such as, " That's all," or, " What's the sum ? "

Practise with the following exercises until the adder can get all the sums correctly in a minute or less. Then the reader must read a column in less than a minute.

43

(1)	(2)	(3)	(4)
$ 3.43	$ 7.43	$ 2.76	$ 3.43
7.16	6.89	5.24	7.72
6.88	5.28	1.84	5.94
8.75	6.16	39.63	3.51
1.99	7.24	8.19	2.67
2.37	8.15	3.55	6.76
4.12	9.91	7.31	1.81
8.56	6.78	26.95	9.38
7.19	1.33	4.27	8.53
9.32	2.75	6.98	6.14
4.53	7.64	85.64	4.29
1.79	6.53	9.48	5.32
6.52	8.39	8.37	7.45
8.68	7.51	52.23	7.98
6.53	1.84	4.59	2.61
51.79	92.29	3.12	49.86
79.32	57.64	6.75	51.55
83.87	74.52	81.86	96.43
16.14	56.35	7.43	28.19
65.64	31.57	6.81	74.88
$ 384.58	$ 406.20	$ 373.00	$ 384.45

(5)	(6)	(7)	(8)
$ 7.42	$ 8.93	$ 7.15	$ 3.43
2.99	2.18	2.69	7.72
8.54	9.26	6.98	4.86
5.63	1.35	5.12	8.99
9.88	2.59	1.24	7.72
1.25	7.32	8.71	3.63
6.48	3.77	2.36	4.46
1.31	8.48	9.51	6.37
4.26	1.81	4.95	2.46
3.65	6.64	3.16	1.72
7.43	4.13	1.28	7.31
6.39	9.85	6.43	8.64
5.98	7.61	7.69	3.55
1.52	5.42	5.82	4.89
2.87	2.53	2.56	1.78
73.64	26.79	93.64	68.35
54.71	26.86	51.81	86.11
66.37	75.98	74.48	59.68
18.16	33.15	15.37	92.59
43.12	94.67	43.82	35.23
$ 331.60	$ 339.32	$ 354.77	$ 419.49

(9)	(10)	(11)	(12)
$ 7.29	$ 5.26	$ 7.18	$ 37.85
6.44	27.45	3.55	9.62
91.23	8.33	6.79	5.23
9.61	5.72	25.21	83.14
2.96	3.56	8.66	2.56
8.17	59.22	5.48	4.49
35.35	1.94	7.25	6.77
4.92	2.68	41.38	8.68
3.83	6.13	3.61	51.33
6.51	84.91	9.25	2.14
5.84	7.88	76.49	8.25
2.93	4.37	4.63	5.97
19.59	3.91	8.92	6.64
1.47	6.88	96.55	29.73
8.17	61.19	7.78	1.85
6.55	9.64	8.54	3.44
73.71	7.37	3.95	64.38
4.86	8.41	51.76	8.72
6.68	12.55	9.39	7.61
67.32	4.76	5.27	5.56
$ 373.43	$ 332.16	$ 391.64	$ 353.96

(13)	(14)	(15)	(16)
$ 6.46	$ 6.46	$ 5.26	$ 7.18
5.22	4.35	27.45	3.55
4.86	3.24	8.33	6.79
8.99	2.18	5.72	25.21
7.72	6.51	3.56	8.66
3.63	9.66	59.22	5.48
4.46	4.73	1.94	7.25
6.37	3.32	2.68	41.38
2.46	5.49	6.13	3.61
1.72	9.17	84.91	9.25
7.31	1.64	7.88	76.49
8.64	8.25	4.37	4.63
3.55	6.78	3.91	8.92
4.89	7.98	6.88	96.55
1.78	1.82	61.19	7.78
68.35	88.53	9.64	8.54
86.11	85.95	7.37	3.95
59.68	67.31	8.41	51.76
92.59	72.82	12.55	9.39
35.23	41.69	4.76	5.27
$ 420.02	$ 437.88	$ 332.16	$ 391.64

Section 4.

Addition by Oneself.

When adding by ourselves we are not dependent upon the accuracy of the one who reads out the numbers. We must learn to see the numbers quickly and transfer them accurately to the abacus.

Practice with this page until you can give all the sums correctly in thirty seconds or less.

(1)	(2)	(3)	(4)	(5)
607	793	812	538	236
158	187	238	662	769
235	775	525	843	582
919	317	413	757	414
670	128	677	432	795
721	304	338	765	521
813	777	672	669	975
585	619	325	334	704
792	531	838	188	813
444	835	180	517	952
5944	5266	5018	5705	6761

$ 7.24	$ 3.83	$ 4.61	$ 8.16
8.35	6.50	3.53	2.57
1.63	9.67	1.86	6.25
2.85	8.18	9.27	9.41
6.89	2.57	1.84	3.24
8.32	6.25	6.89	1.13
6.61	5.19	3.13	7.22
8.87	4.81	8.87	2.65
2.53	3.13	5.92	9.43
8.41	6.53	7.35	6.41
$ 61.70	$ 56.66	$ 53.27	$ 56.47

$ 6.32	$ 2.16	$ 2.18	$ 4.61
2.56	7.77	7.59	3.53
1.12	6.65	1.88	1.86
8.15	3.50	6.35	9.27
2.33	4.68	2.23	1.88
9.59	5.27	5.61	6.89
4.68	9.64	4.16	3.13
5.27	5.61	6.89	1.13
7.97	2.81	2.52	5.92
6.56	8.19	6.93	7.35
$ 54.55	$ 56.28	$ 46.34	$ 45.57

Section 5.

Addition of Figures from Tabulated Forms.

If you wish to add figures which are on separate cards or pages, use the right hand for manipulating the abacus and the left hand to turn the pages.

Sometimes it is convenient to place the pages so that all the numbers can be seen and use a card to cover all except the figures which you wish to add, as is shown in the illustration.

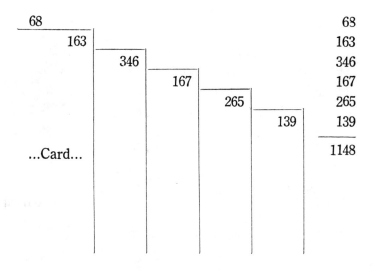

68
163
346
167
265
139
...Card...

68
163
346
167
265
139
1148

Use the following columns for practice in addition. Find the sums and compare your sums with those given below. Do over any columns which you have done incorrectly.

18	86	24	76	26
56	13	99	59	49
74	26	16	68	66
19	42	43	54	82
84	12	56	22	16
56	11	26	11	40
34	90	27	90	91
24	67	19	34	28
46	37	80	67	56
57	56	47	69	94
34	56	34	28	40
19	17	29	16	69
88	96	50	57	69
72	34	49	96	76
27	23	76	74	53
29	78	54	34	36
33	96	28	43	50
17	43	16	37	96
52	51	76	51	95
65	77	54	73	18
13	18	39	41	34
95	35	24	59	57
1012	1064	966	1159	1241

51

Add each column.

$ 4.89	$ 19.58	$ 5.95	$ 71.83
6.12	3.32	62.78	8.69
23.58	85.94	1.27	2.71
9.91	4.86	9.31	54.27
85.73	7.79	8.80	1.36
7.04	8.41	33.41	35.04
74.27	41.15	4.66	8.91
6.82	20.36	7.33	9.59
9.65	6.98	96.29	3.17
31.34	4.27	3.16	97.45
3.91	5.43	77.64	6.83
2.56	73.74	8.91	9.32
97.48	8.35	5.55	45.68
8.75	6.69	86.79	2.91
53.93	32.16	5.40	4.49
5.19	9.23	41.14	3.63
8.32	7.02	4.86	19.87
15.81	5.58	58.79	5.10
1.64	64.67	2.72	6.26
6.20	3.98	9.32	51.81
5.98	6.47	93.63	2.18
27.36	33.39	1.40	13.03
6.09	2.12	5.58	8.59
88.47	1.28	68.17	35.95
1.64	50.84	9.26	67.72
14.51	5.66	5.39	3.30
6.75	4.97	23.91	2.41
9.89	69.52	6.53	21.66
65.18	7.95	40.32	6.81
7.33	5.36	2.82	8.25
696.34	607.07	791.09	618.82

52

Find the sums:

$ 75.53	$ 59.13	$ 16.35	$ 40.52
46.61	14.95	4.97	78.99
1.35	7.38	65.13	9.21
2.20	81.74	9.09	4.82
39.17	2.09	51.42	4.87
2.46	46.65	2.71	5.63
5.42	7.29	5.26	7.18
2.76	6.44	27.45	3.55
1.84	91.23	8.33	6.97
39.63	9.61	5.72	25.21
8.19	2.96	3.56	8.66
3.55	8.17	59.22	5.48
7.31	35.35	1.94	7.25
26.95	4.92	2.69	41.38
4.27	3.83	6.13	3.61
6.98	6.51	84.91	9.25
85.64	5.84	7.88	76.49
9.48	2.93	4.37	4.63
8.39	15.95	3.91	8.92
52.23	1.47	6.88	96.53
4.95	8.12	61.19	7.78
3.12	6.55	9.64	8.54
6.72	73.71	7.37	3.95
81.86	4.86	8.41	51.76
7.34	6.67	12.55	9.39
6.81	67.32	4.89	5.27
37.89	8.64	2.54	8.17
9.62	4.11	3.97	44.66
5.23	23.56	4.89	5.51
83.14	6.93	6.64	7.88
676.64	624.91	500.01	602.06

CHAPTER III.

SUBTRACTION

Subtraction is the process of taking away from something. What is left, or the difference, is called the remainder.

Section 1.

Subtraction Table.

Memorize this table.

$10 - 1 = 9$	One	from	Ten	is	Nine.
$10 - 2 = 8$	Two	from	Ten	is	Eight.
$10 - 3 = 7$	Three	from	Ten	is	Seven.
$10 - 4 = 6$	Four	from	Ten	is	Six.
$10 - 5 = 5$	Five	from	Ten	is	Five.
$10 - 6 = 4$	Six	from	Ten	is	Four.
$10 - 7 = 3$	Seven	from	Ten	is	Three.
$10 - 8 = 2$	Eight	from	Ten	is	Two.
$10 - 9 = 1$	Nine	from	Ten	is	One.

Section 2.

The Practical Use of the Counters
in Subtraction.

You have already learned the method of addition.

Subtraction is just the contrary of addition, but it could be considered the same thing if you think of how much you must add to the subtrahend to make the minuend.

Without knowing it you have already subtracted in doing Example 23 in Section 2 of Addition.

Now I will show you a method of subtraction which is just the same as addition, and if you understand how to handle numbers of one place, it will be easy to calculate the difference between any numbers.

Section 2.

Part 1.

Subtracting with Numbers of One
Place.

Example 1. 1 from 2 is 1.

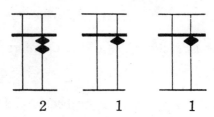

(1) With the thumb raise two Earth counters on the unit position.

(2) Replace one of these with the forefinger.

One is indicated on the board. It is the remainder.

Example 2. 2 from 3 is 1.

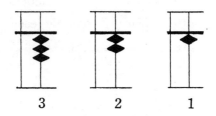

(1) With the thumb raise three Earth counters on the unit upright.

(2) With the forefinger take away two of these.

One is indicated on the board. It is the remainder.

56

Example 3. 3 from 4 is 1.

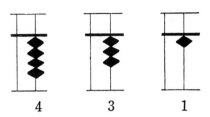

(1) With the thumb raise four Earth counters on the unit upright.

(2) Take away three of these with the forefinger.

One is indicated on the board. It is the remainder.

Example 4. 1 from 6 is 5.

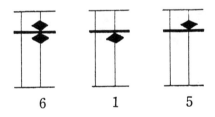

(1) Press between your fingers the Heaven counter and one Earth counter on the unit position.

(2) With the forefinger replace the Earth counter.

Five is indicated on the board. It is the remainder.

Example 5. 2 from 7 is 5.

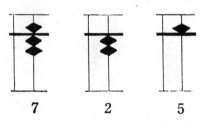

7   2   5

(1) Press between the fingers one Heaven counter and two Earth counters on the unit position.

(2) With the forefinger return the two Earth counters.

5 is indicated on the board. It is the remainder.

Example 6. 3 from 8 is 5.

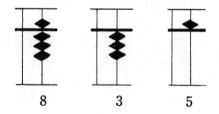

8   3   5

(1) Press between the fingers one Heaven counter and three Earth counters on the unit upright.

(2) Take away the three Earth counters using the forefinger.

5 is indicated on the board. It is the remainder.

Example 7. 4 from 9 is 5.

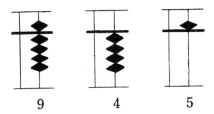

9   4   5

(1) Press between the fingers the Heaven counter and four Earth counters on the unit upright.

(2) With the forefinger take away the four Earth counters.

5 is indicated on the board. It is the remainder.

Example 8. 5 from 6 is 1.

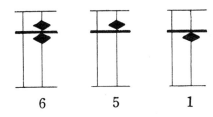

6   5   1

(1) Press between the fingers the Heaven counter and one Earth counter on the unit upright.

(2) Take away the Heaven counter using the forefinger.

1 is indicated on the board. It is the remainder.

Example 9. 5 from 7 is 2.

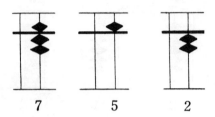

7   5   2

(1) Press between the fingers the Heaven counter and two Earth counters.

(2) With the forefinger replace the Heaven counter.

2 is indicated on the board. It is the remainder.

Example 10. 5 from 8 is 3.

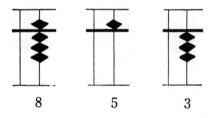

8   5   3

(1) Press between the fingers the Heaven counter and three Earth counters on the unit upright.

(2) With the forefinger replace the Heaven counter.

3 is indicated on the board. It is the remainder.

Example 11. 5 from 9 is 4.

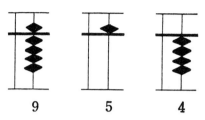

(1) Press between the fingers the Heaven counter and four Earth counters on the unit position.

(2) With the forefinger replace the Heaven counter.

4 is indicated on the board. It is the remainder.

Example 12. 4 from 8 is 4.

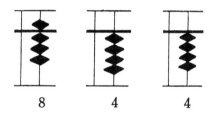

(1) Press between the fingers the Heaven counter and three Earth counters on the unit upright.

(2) Think, "4 from 5 is 1." With the thumb raise one Earth counter on the same upright as the others and at the same time return to place the Heaven counter, using the forefinger.

4 is indicated on the board. It is the remainder.

Example 13. 4 from 7 is 3.

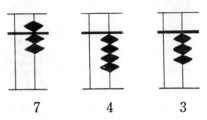

(1) Press between the fingers the Heaven counter and two Earth counters on the unit upright.

(2) Think, "4 from 5 is 1." With the thumb raise one Earth counter on the same upright and at the same time, with the forefinger, return the Heaven counter.

3 is indicated on the board. It is the remainder.

Example 14. 4 from 6 is 2.

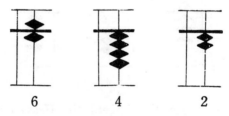

(1) Press between the fingers the Heaven counter and one Earth counter on the unit upright.

(2) Think, "4 from 5 is 1." With the thumb raise one Earth counter on the same upright and at the same time, using the forefinger, return to place the Heaven counter.

2 is indicated on the board. It is the remainder.

Example 15. 3 from 7 is 4.

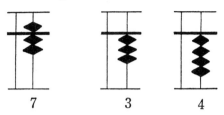

(1) Press between the fingers the Heaven counter and two Earth counters on the unit upright.

(2) Think, "3 from 5 is 2." With the thumb raise two Earth counters on the same upright and, using the forefinger, return the Heaven counter.

4 is indicated on the board. It is the remainder.

Example 16. 3 from 6 is 3.

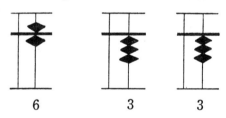

(1) Press between the fingers the Heaven counter and one Earth counter on the unit upright.

(2) Think, "3 from 5 is 2." With the thumb raise two Earth counters on the same upright, and, using the forefinger, replace the Heaven counter.

3 is indicated on the board. It is the remainder.

Example 17. 2 from 6 is 4.

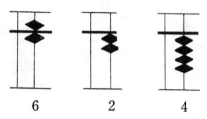

6   2   4

(1) Press between the fingers the Heaven counter and one Earth counter on the unit upright.

(2) Think, "2 from 5 is 3." With the thumb raise three Earth counters on the same upright, and at the same time, using the forefinger, return to place the Heaven counter.

4 is indicated on the board. It is the remainder.

Example 18. 1 from 5 is 4.

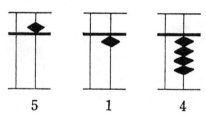

5   1   4

(1) With the forefinger slide down the Heaven counter on the unit upright.

(2) Think, "1 from 5 is 4." With the thumb raise four Earth counters on the same upright and, using the forefinger, return to place the Heaven counter.

4 is indicated on the board. It is the remainder.

Example 19. 2 from 5 is 3.

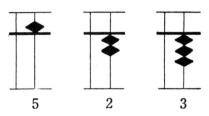

5   2   3

(1) With the forefinger slide down the Heaven counter on the unit upright.

(2) Think, "2 from 5 is 3." With the thumb raise three Earth counters on the same upright and at the same time, using the forefinger, return the Heaven counter to place.

3 is indicated on the board. It is the remainder.

Example 20. 3 from 5 is 2.

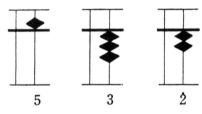

5   3   2

(1) With the forefinger slide down the Heaven counter on the unit upright.

(2) Think, "3 from 5 is 2." With the thumb raise two Earth counters on the same upright and at the same time, with the forefinger, return the Heaven counter to place.

2 is indicated on the board. It is the remainder.

Example 21. 4 from 5 is 1.

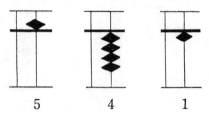

5   4   1

(1) With the forefinger slide down the Heaven counter on the unit upright.

(2) Think, " 4 from 5 is 1." With the thumb raise one Earth counter on the same upright, and at the same time, with the forefinger, return the Heaven counter to place.

1 is indicated on the board. It is the remainder.

Example 22. 6 from 9 is 3.

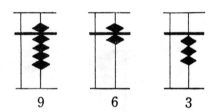

9   6   3

(1) Press between the fingers the Heaven counter and four Earth counters on the unit upright.

(2) At one time return the Heaven counter with the forefinger and one Earth counter with the thumb. The remainder is three.

Notice that in these cases when we return a Heaven counter and an Earth counter at the same time we must use two fingers.

Example 23. 6 from 8 is 2.

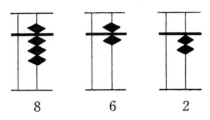

(1) Press between the fingers one Heaven counter and three Earth counters on the unit upright.

(2) Return to place the Heaven counter and one of the Earth counters at the same time, using both forefinger and thumb.

2 is indicated on the board. It is the remainder.

Example 24. 6 from 7 is 1.

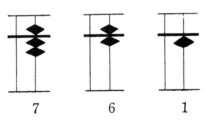

(1) Press between the fingers one Heaven counter and two Earth counters on the unit upright.

(2) Return to place the Heaven counter and one Earth counter at the same time, using both forefinger and thumb.

1 is indicated on the board. It is the remainder.

Example 25. 7 from 9 is 2.

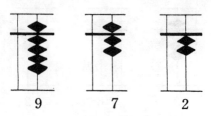

(1) Press between the fingers the Heaven counter and four Earth counters on the unit upright.

(2) Return to place the Heaven counter and two of the Earth counters at the same time, using the forefinger and the thumb.

2 is indicated on the board. It is the remainder.

Example 26. 7 from 8 is 1.

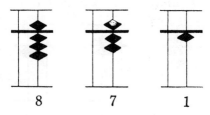

(1) Press between the fingers the Heaven counter and three Earth counters on the unit upright.

(2) Return to place the Heaven counter and two of the Earth counters at the same time, using the forefinger and the thumb.

1 is indicated on the board. It is the remainder.

Example 27. 8 from 9 is 1.

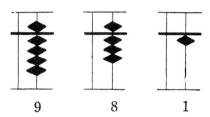

| 9 | 8 | 1 |

(1) Press between the fingers the Heaven counter and four Earth counters on the unit upright.

(2) Return to place the Heaven counter and three of the Earth counters at one time, using the forefinger and the thumb.

1 is indicated on the board. It is the remainder.

In a general way this completes the method of subtraction.

Although we have dealt with numbers of one place only, using this method as a criterion, we can now subtract larger numbers.

As the method of determining the position on the board, and of handling the counters is practically the same as that of addition, I will abbreviate my explanations.

In these exercises the abbreviation "S. T.", means "Subtraction Tables."

Section 2.

Part 2.

Subtracting with Large Numbers.

Example 1. 1 from 10 is 9.

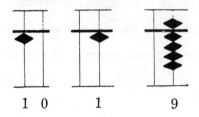

(1) With the thumb raise one Earth counter on the next upright to the left of the unit upright. This indicates ten.

(2) Think, " S. T. 1 from 10 is 9." With the forefinger return the Earth counter on the 10 upright and press between your fingers the Heaven counter and four Earth counters on the unit upright.

9 is indicated on the board. It is the remainder.

Example 2. 2 from 10 is 8.

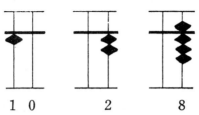

1 0   2   8

(1) With the thumb raise one Earth counter on the next upright to the left of the unit upright. This indicates 10.

(2) Think, "S. T. 2 from 10 is 8." Replace the Earth counter on the 10 upright, with the forefinger. Then press between your fingers the Heaven counter and three Earth counters of the unit upright.

8 is indicated on the board. It is the remainder.

Example 3. 2 from 11 is 9.

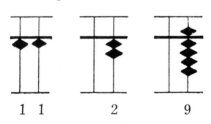

1 1   2   9

(1) With the thumb raise one counter on the 10 upright.

(2) With the thumb raise one Earth counter on the unit upright. 11 is now indicated on the board.

71

(3) Think, "S. T. 2 from 10 is 8." Return to place the Earth counter on the 10 upright and then press between the fingers the Heaven counter and three Earth counters on the unit upright.

9 is indicated on the board. It is the remainder.

Example 4. 3 from 10 is 7.

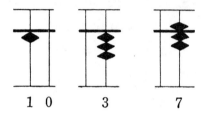

1 0   3   7

(1) With the thumb raise one Earth counter on the 10 upright.

(2) Think, "S. T. 3 from 10 is 7." With the forefinger replace the Earth counter on the 10 upright and press between the fingers the Heaven counter and three Earth counters on the unit upright.

7 is indicated on the board. It is the remainder.

Example 5. 3 from 11 is 8.

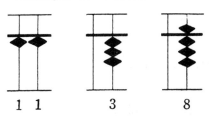

1 1   3   8

(1) Raise one Earth counter on the 10 upright, with the thumb.

(2) With the thumb also raise one Earth counter on the unit upright. 11 is now indicated on the board.

(3) Think, " S. T. 3 from 10 is 7." With the forefinger return to place the Earth counter on the 10 upright and then press between the fingers the Heaven counter and two Earth counters on the unit upright.

8 is indicated on the board. It is the remainder.

Example 6. 3 from 12 is 9.

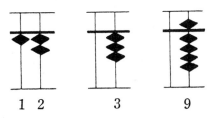

1 2   3   9

(1) With the thumb raise one Earth counter on the 10 upright.

(2) Raise two Earth counters on the unit upright with the thumb. 12 is now indicated.

(3) Think, " S. T. 3 from 10 is 7." With the forefinger return to place the Earth counter on the 10 upright, then press between the fingers the Heaven counter and two Earth counters on the unit upright.

9 is indicated on the board. It is the remainder.

Example 7. 5 from 14 is 9.

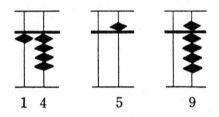

1 4   5   9

(1) With the thumb raise one Earth counter on the 10 upright.

(2) With the thumb raise four Earth counters on the unit upright. 14 is now indicated.

(3) Think, " S. T. 5 from 10 is 5." Return to place the Earth counter on the 10 upright, using the forefinger and then slide down the Heaven counter on the unit upright.

9 is indicated on the board. It is the remainder.

74

Example 8. 4 from 11 is 7.

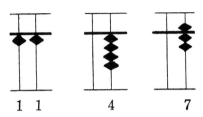

| 1 1 | 4 | 7 |

(1)   Raise one Earth counter on the 10 upright with the thumb.

(2)   With the thumb also, raise one Earth counter on the unit upright. 11 is now indicated.

(3)   Think, " S. T. 4 from 10 is 6." With the forefinger return to place the Earth counter on the 10 upright. Then press between the fingers the Heaven counter and one Earth counter on the unit upright.

7 is indicated on the board. It is the remainder.

Example 9. 4 from 13 is 9.

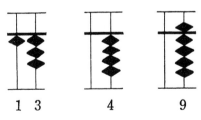

| 1 3 | 4 | 9 |

(1)   With thumb raise one Earth counter on the 10 upright.

(2) With the thumb raise three Earth counters on the unit upright.

(3) Think, "S. T. 4 from 10 is 6." With the forefinger return to place the Earth counter on the 10 upright and then press between the fingers the Heaven counter, and one Earth counter on the unit upright.

9 is indicated on the board. It is the remainder.

Example 10. 5 from 11 is 6.

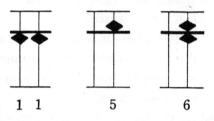

1 1   5   6

(1) With the thumb raise one Earth counter on the 10 upright.

(2) With the thumb raise one Earth counter on the unit upright. 11 is now indicated on the board.

(3) Think, "S. T. 5 from 10 is 5." With the forefinger return to place the Earth counter on the 10 upright and then slide down the Heaven counter on the unit upright.

6 is indicated on the board. It is the remainder.

Example 11. 6 from 12 is 6.

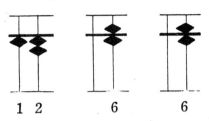

1 2   6   6

(1) Raise one Earth counter on the ten upright with the thumb.

(2) Raise two Earth counters on the unit upright with the thumb. 12 is now indicated.

(3) Think, "S. T. 6 from 10 is 4," and "A. T. 4 and 1 are 5." Replace the Earth counter on the ten upright with the forefinger and then at one time, slide down the Heaven counter on the unit upright and return one Earth counter on the same upright with the forefinger.

Six is indicated on the board. It is the remainder.

Example 12. 7 from 13 is 6.

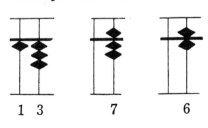

1 3   7   6

(1) Raise one Earth counter on the ten upright with the thumb.

(2) Raise three Earth counters on the unit upright with the thumb.

13 is now indicated on the board.

(3) Think, "S. T. 7 from 10 is 3 and A. T. 3 and 2 are 5." With the forefinger return to place the Earth counter on the ten upright and then at the same time take down the Heaven counter on the unit upright and return to place two Earth counters on the same upright, with the forefinger.

6 is indicated on the board. It is the remainder.

Example 13. 8 from 14 is 6.

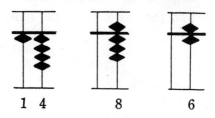

1 4   8   6

(1) With the thumb raise one Earth counter on the ten upright.

(2) With the thumb raise four Earth counters on the unit upright.

(3)   Think, " S. T. 8 from 10 is 2 and A. T. 2 and 3 are 5." With the forefinger return to place the Earth counter on the ten upright.   At one time with the forefinger slide down the Heaven counter on the unit upright and return to place three of the Earth counters on the same upright.

6 is indicated on the board.   It is the remainder.

Example 14. 9 from 16 is 7.

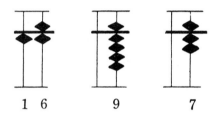

1   6   9   7

(1)   With the thumb raise one Earth counter on the ten upright.

(2)   Press between the fingers the Heaven counter and one Earth counter on the unit upright.

16 is now indicated on the board.

(3)   Think, " S. T. 9 from 10 is 1." With the forefinger return to place the Earth counter on the ten upright and raise one Earth counter on the unit upright, using the thumb.

7 is indicated on the board.   It is the difference.

Example 15. 99 from 100 is 1.

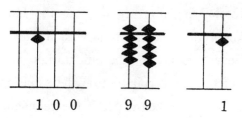

1 0 0   9 9   1

(1) With the thumb raise one Earth counter on the second upright to the left of the unit upright. This indicates 100.

(2) Think, "S. T. 9 from 10 is 1." Return to place the Earth counter on the 100 upright with the forefinger and at the same time with the thumb, raise one Earth counter on the ten upright.

(3) Think, "S. T. 9 from 10 is 1." With the forefinger return to place the Earth counter on the ten upright and then raise one Earth counter on the unit upright.

1 is indicated on the board. It is the remainder.

The above illustrations give practical examples of subtraction with numbers of two places or more. These will show that if you clearly understand subtracting with small numbers, it will be easy for you to handle any number.

In the following exercises find the remainders and write them in position. Check your answers by adding the remainder to the number above it. The sum should be the top number.

Row A.	$ 9.24	$ 5.34	$ 6.85	$ 23.74
	6.68	2.77	3.49	16.88.

Row B.	$ 86.03	$ 19.35	$ 24.83	$ 40.52
	76.18	17.84	18.99	24.66

Row C.	$ 2748.36	$ 6025.04	$ 6491.32
	1977.69	4749.27	5943.74

Row D.	$ 1002.30	$ 7341.72	$ 5372.07
	974.64	6488.84	4493.19

Row E.	$ 190.04	$ 43.65	$ 163.28
	111.15	27.89	156.49

Row F.	$ 227.41	$ 395.26	$ 1735.62
	166.83	107.48	1448.83

Subtract and write in the remainders.

Row A.	66	66	87	55	44	74
	23	42	43	34	36	46

Row B.	229	175	408	553	387
	154	86	234	378	299

Row C.	15	13	123	897	789	21
	8	9	98	121	667	14

Row D.	100	1767	2325	5566	4858
	89	989	1936	3179	4075

Checking Errors in Subtraction.

As was stated before, it is always good to check your answer in subtraction by adding the remainder to the subtrahend, which should give you the minuend.

The following illustrations will make this clear:

67	Minuend	39	Difference
28	Subtrahend	28	Subtrahend
39	Difference	67	Minuend

Section 3.

Subtraction in Cases Where the Subtrahend is Larger than the Minuend.

In such cases we place the subtrahend on the board first and subtract from it the minuend. The result is called the remainder but must be preceded by the minus sign.

Example 1. 7 from 3 is −4.

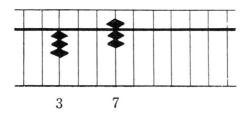

3   7

(1) With the thumb raise three Earth counters on an upright in the left half of the abacus.

(2) Press between the fingers one Heaven counter and two Earth counters on an upright in the right half of the abacus.

(3) Because the subtrahend 7 is larger than the minuend 3, we must subtract the minuend from the subtrahend.

Think, "3 from 5 is 2." Raise two Earth counters on

83

the same upright where 7 is indicated and at the same time return to place the Heaven counter of the same upright.

4 is indicated on the board. It is the remainder if it is preceded by the minus sign.

There is a simpler way to subtract when the subtrahend is larger than the minuend.

Example 2. 9 from 8 is –1.

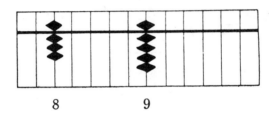

8   9

When we subtract 9 from 8, because the 9 is larger than the 8, we can assume that there is one Earth counter raised on the next upright to the left from the unit upright on which 8 is indicated. In other words we assume that we have 18 on the board and then we subtract 9 from 18.

(1) Press between the fingers the Heaven counter and three Earth counters on the unit upright.

(2) Now we are ready to assume that we have ten more than we have, so we raise one Earth counter on the upright to the left of the one where 8 is indicated. 18 is now indicated.

(3) Think, "9 from 10 is 1." With the forefinger return to place the Earth counter on the ten upright and raise one Earth counter on the unit upright, with the thumb. 9 is indicated on the board.

(4) But we have assumed that we have ten more than we really have. Therefore 10 must be subtracted from the 9, leaving us –1.

Whenever we assume that we have 10 or 100 or 1000 more than we really have, we must always subtract this number, which we have assumed, from the remainder, which we get. The difference between these two is the real remainder and is always preceded by a minus sign. It is called the "supplementary number." The following table shows some supplementary numbers:

The supplementary number of	9	is	1.
,,	,,	8	is	2.
,,	,,	3	is	7.
,,	,,	23	is	77.
,,	,,	567	is	433.
,,	,,	4321	is	5679.

(5) In this case our remainder was 9. The supplementary number of 9 is 1. Therefore, the real remainder is –1.

In the above case we were subtracting with numbers of one place, therefore, we assumed we had ten extra. In subtracting numbers of two places we assume that we have 100 extra, etc.

Find the difference between the lower number and the upper number in the following examples. Lay a strip of paper across the page and write the answers on it. Check your answers with those given.

Practice with these examples until you can do a row or nearly a row in a minute and get them all right.

Row A.	535	430	200	6ŏ2	239	453
	−278	−192	−135	−483	−171	−335
	257	238	65	179	68	118

Row B.	752	91	87	325	560	97
	−384	−46	−73	−158	−290	−35
	368	45	14	167	270	62

Row C.	357	528	812	200	998	677
	−159	−379	−576	−157	−372	−257
	198	149	236	43	626	420

Write the difference, making sure that each remainder is right by adding it to the subtrahend.

Row D.	$ 6.74	$ 9.03	$ 7.59	$ 4.59
	−3.21	−4.09	−6.52	−2.39

Review.

Addition and Subtraction in combination.

Give as many right answers as you can in a minute.

(1)	(2)	(3)	(4)	(5)
$ 24.72	$ 1.52	$ 222.33	$ 51.82	$ 45.58
12.15	− .73	−34.54	671.35	6.63
−9.98	− .32	− 9.93	78.56	112.96
3.21	13.54	−18.97	−442.84	− 10.07
17.05	52.53	−66.26	− 77.15	− 55.99
75.37	5.51	−31.74	− 19.91	101.20
−21.12	−20.03	−13.80	627.84	70.81
4.51	7.94	−29.17	−791.17	22.56
22.37	13.49	− 8.33	− 84.91	18.73
−44.78	4.44	− 6.66	44.44	−203.52
− 7.11	−17.19	2.52	21.47	− 39.99
18.36	− 3.24	4.65	377.99	131.10
7.71	41.82	17.92	222.35	− 73.75
18.01	15.92	1.88	− 97.14	27.75
1.01	16.99	10.10	− 24.58	18.49
−91.38	− 75.91	4.57	121.43	13.18
40.51	34.88	5.35	240.52	526.17
−21.22	− 42.27	− 14.43	99.13	288.04
−35.53	− 19.99	− 18.19	− 27.32	−444.44
6.16	− 18.90	2.02	− 18.62	−189.44
$ 20.02	$ 10.00	$ 19.32	$973.26	$366.00

Balancing of

Receipts and Expenditures.

Date	Receipts	Expenditures	+ or −	Balance
1	$ 5762.61	$ 3473.49	+	$ 2289.12
2	937.54	658.35	+	279.19
3	48.15	239.98	−	191.83
4	619.50	422.60	+	196.90
5	2544.32	1945.73	+	598.59
6	91.02	877.41	−	786.39
7	793.67	682.85	+	110.82
8	214.86	122.40	+	92.46
9	6022.33	4751.45	+	1270.88
10	214.86	122.40	+	92.46
11	85.27	471.37	−	386.10
12	151.93	99.16	+	52.77
13	830.24	561.58	+	268.66
14	2481.10	3354.37	−	873.27
15	65.83	29.41	+	36.42
16	229.48	198.46	+	31.02
17	5216 77	6627.18	−	1410.41
18	889.63	792.53	+	97.10
19	510.33	798.46	−	288.13
20	78.49	66.82	+	11.67
21	114.85	203.55	−	88.70
22	862.00	750.43	+	111.57
23	1284.56	2114.85	−	830.29
24	772.09	976.48	−	204.39
25	3740.10	2963.38	+	776.72
26	101.66	310.55	−	208.89
27	563.28	93.62	+	469.66
28	1529.47	1003.41	+	526.06
29	209.53	2133.46	−	1923.93
30	773.37	471.20	+	302.17
	37738.84	37316.93		421.91

CHAPTER IV.

MULTIPLICATION

There are two methods of multiplication on the abacus in general use at the present time. By one method we begin to multiply the last figures in each of the numbers together, but in the other method we begin by multiplying the first figure of one number with the last figure of the other.

The first of these methods is called, "Multiplication Beginning at the Right."

The second of these methods is called, "Multiplication Beginning at the Left."

18	Multiplicand
9	Multiplier
162	Product

In "Multiplication Beginning at the Right" we begin the multiplication by multiplying the last figure of the multiplier and the last figure of the multiplicand and continue working to the left.

In "Multiplication Beginning at the Left" we begin our multiplication by multiplying the first figure of the multiplier and the last figure of the multiplicand, working to the left in the multiplicand and to the right in the multiplier.

The first of these methods, "Multiplication Beginning at the Right" is convenient because it is already familiar to us in ordinary multiplication, but the other method, "Multiplication Beginning at the Left", is really more convenient, if by practice we become skilful in it.

By explanation I shall try to show you both of these methods.

Section 1.

Multiplication Table.

In this section the abbreviation "M. T." stands for Multiplication Table. It is very important for you to memorize this table.

Multiplication Table.

M. T. of 1.				M. T. of 2.			
1 × 1	is	1.		2 × 2	is	4.
1 × 2	is	2.		2 × 3	is	6.
1 × 3	is	3.		2 × 4	is	8.
1 × 4	is	4.		2 × 5	is	10.
1 × 5	is	5.		2 × 6	is	12.
1 × 6	is	6.		2 × 7	is	14.
1 × 7	is	7.		2 × 8	is	16.
1 × 8	is	8.		2 × 9	is	18.
1 × 9	is	9.				

90

M. T. of 3.			
3	× 3	is	9.
3	× 4	is	12.
3	× 5	is	15.
3	× 6	is	18.
3	× 7	is	21.
3	× 8	is	24.
3	× 9	is	27.

M. T. of 4.			
4	× 4	is	16.
4	× 5	is	20.
4	× 6	is	24.
4	× 7	is	28.
4	× 8	is	32.
4	× 9	is	36.

M. T. of 5.			
5	× 5	is	25.
5	× 6	is	30.
5	× 7	is	35.
5	× 8	is	40.
5	× 9	is	45.

M. T. of 6.			
6	× 6	is	36.
6	× 7	is	42.
6	× 8	is	48.
6	× 9	is	54.

M. T. of 7.			
7	× 7	is	49.
7	× 8	is	56.
7	× 9	is	63.

M. T. of 8.			
8	× 8	is	64.
8	× 9	is	72.

M. T. of 9.			
9	× 9	is	81.

When you multiply two numbers, you must constantly keep in mind the Multiplication Table. And sometimes it is even convenient to say it out loud while manipulating the counters.

Section 2.

Determination of Position in Multiplication.

When we multiply two numbers we set the multiplier on the lefthand side and the multiplicand to the right of it. Then we must determine the unit position of the product.

Count the number of uprights in the multiplier. Count off the same number of uprights from the multiplicand towards the right. The last one is the unit position for the product.

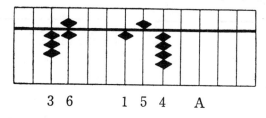

3 6   1 5 4   A

In the above illustration the A upright is the unit upright of the product.

36   multiplier
154   multiplicand

In this case two uprights are necessary to indicate the multiplier. Therefore, we count off two uprights from the multiplicand, and the second one is the unit position of the product.

Section 3.

Multiplication Beginning at the Right.

This is a method of multiplication which prevails at the present time.

When we begin to multiply by this method, we first multiply the righthand figure of the multiplier by the righthand figure of the multiplicand, gradually working to the left.

Part 1.

The Process of Multiplication.

(1) We must indicate the multiplicand on the righthand side of the board, leaving space for the product. And we must indicate the multiplier on the lefthand side of the board.

(2) As was stated before we must count the number of uprights in the multiplier, then count off an equal number of uprights to the right of the multiplicand.

The last one is the unit position for the product.

Now you are ready to begin the multiplication.

(1) Multiply the end figure of the multiplicand by the end figure of the multiplier according to the Multiplication Table.

(2) If we get a product of two places such as 32, we must indicate the two on the unit position of the product by raising two Earth counters, and indicate the three on the upright to the left of the unit one by raising three Earth counters.

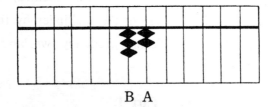

B A

A   is the upright for the unit position

B   is the upright for 10's

(3) Multiply the figure on the ten upright of the multiplier and the end figure of the multiplicand, using the Multiplication Table.

(4) If we should get a product of one place such as 6, we must indicate the 6, on the ten position of the product.

(5)   If we should get a product of two places, such as 45, we must indicate the 5 on the ten upright and the four on the hundred upright of the product as in the following:

C   B   A

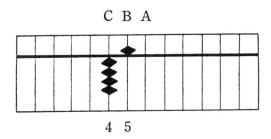

4 5

A   is the upright for ones
B   is the upright for tens
C   is the upright for hundreds

Continuing like this we will come to the place where we will have multiplied the end figure of the multiplicand by every figure of the multiplier, then we must begin to multiply the next figure of the multiplicand by each figure of the multiplier.

When we have multiplied every figure of the multiplicand by every figure of the multiplier the product is indicated on the board.

Part 2

Example 1.   56   multiplicand
                    6   multiplier
                  336   product

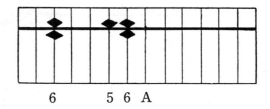

    6   5 6 A

In this case A is the unit upright of the product.

(1) Indicate the multiplier on the lefthand side of the board and the multiplicand to the right of it, as shown in the above illustration.

(2) There is one upright in the multiplier, therefore, the first upright to the right of the multiplicand is the unit upright of the product.

(3) Multiplying the end figures of the multiplier and the multiplicand we get, "6×6 is 36."

(4) Return to place the Heaven counter and the Earth counter on the unit position of the multiplicand, and then

raise three Earth counters on this upright, which is the position for tens in the product, and press between the fingers the Heaven counter and one Earth counter on the next upright to the right, which is the unit position of the product. 536 is now indicated.

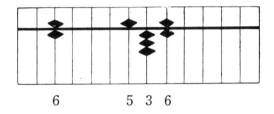

(5) As there is only one figure in the multiplier we are now ready to multiply the multiplier and the second figure of the multiplicand, which is 5. "6×5 is 30."

(6) Return the Heaven counter on the first upright of the multiplicand and raise three Earth counters on the same upright, as it is the upright for 100's in the product.

336 is indicated on the board. It is the product.

Example 2.   56   multiplicand
                   12   multiplier
                  ─────
                  672   product

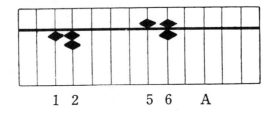

1 2   5 6   A

(1) Indicate the multiplier on the lefthand side of the board and the multiplicand on the righthand side as shown in the above illustration.

(2) There are two uprights in the multiplier, therefore, count off two uprights to the right of the multiplicand to find the unit position of the product.

(3) Multiply the end figure of the multiplicand by the end figure of the multiplier, "6×2 is 12."

(4) Raise one Earth counter on the upright for tens in the product and raise two Earth counters on the unit upright of the product. 5612 is indicated on the board.

98

A

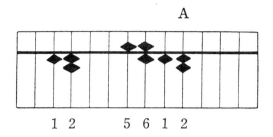

1 2   5 6 1 2

(5) Next multiply the 1 of the multiplier and the 6 of the multiplicand. This gives us "1×6 is 6."

(6) Because we have now multiplied each figure of the multiplier by the figure 6 of the multiplicand, we must now return these counters to place. But we have not yet indicated on the board the product 6 which we got by multiplying the first figure of the multiplier by the last figure of the multiplicand. We now indicate this 6 on the upright for 10's of the product. 5072 should now be indicated on the board.

A

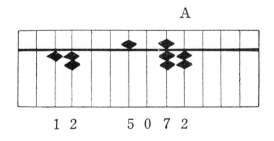

1 2   5 0 7 2

(7) We are now ready to multiply the first figure of the multiplicand, 5, with the end figure of the multiplier. "5×2 is 10."

(8) Raise one Earth counter on the upright for 100's in the product. 5172 should now be indicated on the board.

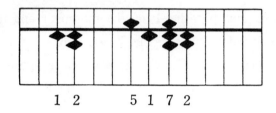

1 2   5 1 7 2

(9) We now multiply the 5 of the multiplicand and the figure 1 of the multiplier. "5×1 is 5."

(10) Because we have multiplied the figure 5 of the multiplicand by each figure of the multiplier we now return to place this 5. Then we must indicate the product 5 which we have just gotten. It must be placed on the upright for 100's in the product.

672 is now indicated on the board. It is the product.

Example 3.   142   multiplicand

               95   multiplier

           13490   product

A

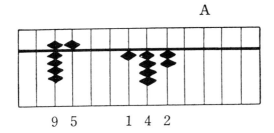

9   5   1   4   2

(1) Indicate the multiplier 95 on the lefthand side of the board and the multiplicand 142 on the right of it, as is shown in the above illustration.

(2) As there are two uprights in the multiplier, count off two places to the right of the multiplicand. This determines the position for the units of the product.

(3) Multiply the end figure of the multiplicand and the end figure of the multiplier. "2×5 is 10."

(4) Raise one Earth counter on the 10 upright of the product, and 14210 will be indicated on the board.

101

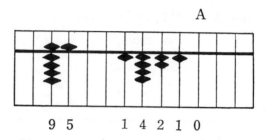

9 5   1 4 2 1 0

(5) We must now multiply the last figure of the multiplicand which is 2, by the first figure of the multiplier, which is 9. " 2×9 is 18."

(6) Because we have multiplied the end figure of the multiplicand by every figure of the multiplier, we are now ready to return to place the counters which indicate this end figure, which is 2. But we can see that the 1 of the product 18 must be indicated on the same upright with the 2 which we are ready to erase, so we return to place only 1 of the Earth counters, leaving 1 to indicate the 1 of 18. Then on the next upright to the right, we indicate the 8 by pressing between our fingers 1 Heaven counter and three Earth counters. 14190 should now be indicated on the board.

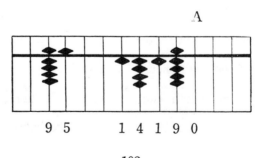

A

9 5   1 4 1 9 0

(7) We are now ready to multiply the second figure of the multiplicand by the multiplier. Multiplying the end figure of the multiplier with the second figure of the multiplicand we get, "4×5 is 20."

(8) Raise two Earth counters on the upright for 100's in the product. 14390 should now be indicated.

A

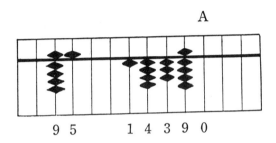

9 5   1 4 3 9 0

(9) The second figure of the multiplicand must now be multiplied by the first figure of the multiplier, that is, "4×9 is 36."

(10) Instead of returning all four of the counters in the figure 4 which we no longer need, we take away only one, leaving three to indicate the 30 of 36, and then indicate 6 on the next upright to the right. 13990 should now be indicated on the board.

A

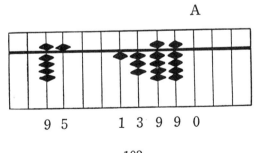

9 5   1 3 9 9 0

(11)   Our next step is to begin to multiply the first figure of the multiplicand by the end figure of the multiplier.   "1×5 is 5."

(12)   We wish to indicate this 5 on the upright for 100's in the product but 9 is indicated already. Therefore, we return to place the Heaven counter and raise one Earth counter on the next upright to the left. 14490 should now be indicated on the board.

A

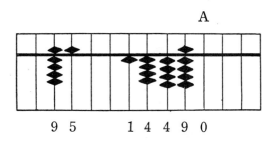

9 5   1 4 4 9 0

(13)   We must now multiply the 1, which is the first figure of the multiplicand, and 9 which is the first figure of the multiplier.   "9×1 is 9."

(14)   As we have now finished with the 1 of the multiplicand, we return this counter to place.

(15)   We are now ready to indicate the product which we got in step 13. This 9 should be placed on the upright for 1000's in the product, but as that upright is already almost full it is easier to replace one Earth counter on the upright

for 1000's and at the same time raise one Earth counter on the next upright to the left.

13490 is indicated on the board. It is the product.

A

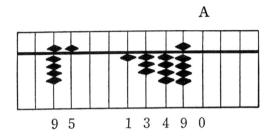

9 5   1 3 4 9 0

Part 3.

Examples for Practice.

Exercise 1.   53 multiplicand
                  7 multiplier
              371 product

A

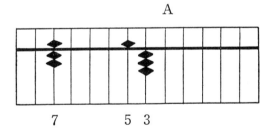

7   5 3

(1) Indicate the multiplier 7 on the lefthand side of the abacus, and to the right of it, the multiplicand 53.

105

(2) As there is only one upright in the multiplier, the first upright on the right of the multiplicand becomes the unit position of the product.

(3) Multiplying the end figure of the multiplicand by the multiplier we get, "3×7 is 21."

(4) As the multiplier is a number of one place only, we no longer need the figure 3 of the multiplicand. But as the 2 of our product 21 must be indicated on the same upright on which the 3 is now indicated, we return to place only one of these Earth counters, leaving two to indicate the 20 of 21. We then raise one Earth counter on the unit upright. 521 should now be indicated on the board.

A

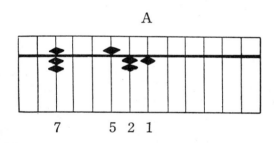

7   5 2 1

(5) We must now multiply the 5 which is the second figure of the multiplicand with the multiplier. This gives us "5×7 is 35."

(6) Return to place the figure 5 of the multiplicand, as the multiplier is a one place number and we have no further use for the 5. Raise three Earth counters on this same upright as it is the upright for 100's in the product. Then

slide down the 5 counter of the next upright to the right, the position for 10's in the product.

371 is indicated on the board. It is the product.

A

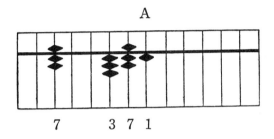

7   3 7 1

Exercise 2. 232   multiplicand
6   multiplier
1392   product

A

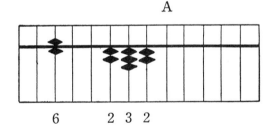

6   2 3 2

(1) On the lefthand side of the abacus indicate the multiplier 6, and to the right of it the multiplicand 232, as is shown in the above illustration.

(2) As there is only one upright in the multiplier, the

next upright to the right of the multiplicand is the unit position for the product.

(3) Multiplying the end figure of the multiplicand by the multiplier, we get, "2×6 is 12."

(4) As the multiplier is a figure of one place, we have no further use for the figure 2 of the multiplicand. But as we must place the 1 of the number 12 on this upright, as it is the position for 10's in the product, we return to place only one of the two counters. Then we raise two Earth counters on the unit upright of the product. 2312 should now be indicated on the board.

(5) We are now ready to multiply the second figure of the multiplicand by the multiplier. This gives us, "3×6 is 18."

(6) We now have no further use for the figure 3 of the multiplicand, but before returning these three counters to place we remember that the 1 of 18 must be indicated on that same upright, as it is the position for 100's in the product. Therefore, we return to place only two of the three Earth counters. Then we press between the fingers the Heaven counter and three Earth counters on the next upright to the right, or the upright for 10's in the product. 2192 is now indicated on the board.

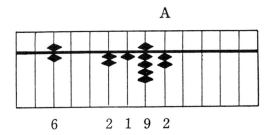

A

6 2 1 9 2

(7) We are now ready to multiply the one remaining figure of the multiplicand by the multiplier. This gives us, " 2×6 is 12."

(8) We no longer need the figure 2 indicated on the board, but as we must indicate the 1 of 12 on the same upright we return to place only one of the two counters. Then we raise two Earth counters on the next upright to the right to indicate the 2 of 12.

1392 is indicated on the board. It is the product.

In the United States one dollar ($ 1.00) is equal to one hundred cents (100¢). When multiplying with figures representing money, do not think of the decimal point until you have gotten the product. Then place the decimal point between the position for 10's and for 100's. This will give you the figure in dollars and cents.

Exercise 3. $ 5.13   multiplicand

.23   multiplier

$ 117.99   product

A

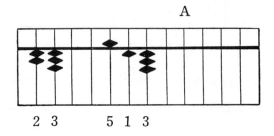

2 3   5 1 3

(1) Indicate the multiplier 23 on the lefthand side of the board. To the right of it indicate the multiplicand 513, as shown in the above illustration.

(2) As there are two uprights in the multiplier, the second upright from the multiplicand to the right, is the upright for the unit position of the product.

(3) The end figure of the multiplicand multiplied by the end figure of the multiplier gives us, "3×3 is 9."

(4) Press between the fingers the Heaven counter and four Earth counters on the unit position of the product. 51309 is indicated on the board.

110

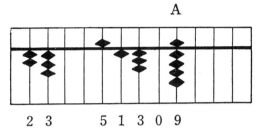

A

2 3   5 1 3 0 9

(5) As the multiplier is a two place number we must next multiply the end figure of the multiplicand by the second figure of the multiplier. This gives us, "3×2 is 6."

(6) We have now finished with the figure 3 of the multiplicand, so we return these three counters to place. Then we press between our fingers the Heaven counter and one Earth counter on the upright for 10's in the product. 51069 is now indicated on the board.

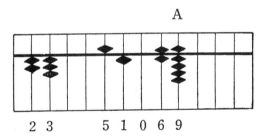

A

2 3   5 1 0 6 9

(7) We are now ready to multiply the second figure of the multiplicand with the end figure of the multiplier. This gives us, "1×3 is 3."

111

(8) Raise three Earth counters on the upright for 10's in the product. 51099 should now be indicated on the board.

A

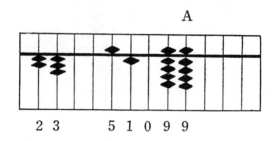

2 3   5 1 0 9 9

(9) Next we must multiply the 1 of the multiplicand with the second figure of the multiplier. This gives us, "1×2 is 2."

(10) As we have no further use for the one of the multiplicand, we return it to place and raise two Earth counters on the next upright to the right, which is the place for 100's in the product. 50299 should be indicated on the board.

A

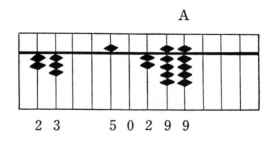

2 3   5 0 2 9 9

(11) Multiplying the first figure of the multiplicand by the end figure of the multiplier we get, "5×3 is 15."

(12) Raise one Earth counter on the upright for 1000's in the product and slide down the Heaven counter on the upright for 100's in the product. 51799 should be indicated on the board.

A

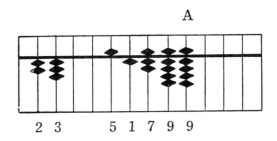

2 3   5 1 7 9 9

(13) Multiplying the first figure of the multiplicand by the first figure of the multiplier we get, "5×2 is 10."

(14) As we now have no further use for the first figure of the multiplicand, we must return it to place. Next we raise one Earth counter on the upright for 10,000's in the product to indicate the 10 which we got in step 13.

11799 is now indicated on the board. This is the product.

113

A

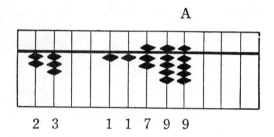

2 3 1 1 7 9 9

Now we must place a decimal point between the upright for 10's and the upright for 100's in the product.

The product will then be indicated as $117.99.

In just this way, you can multiply any numbers large or small.

Exercise 4. 2519 multiplicand
              43 multiplier
          108317 product

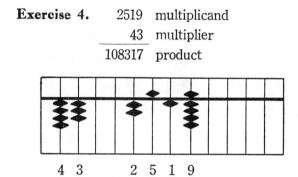

4 3 2 5 1 9

(1) Indicate the multiplier 43 on the lefthand side of the board, and to the right of it the multiplicand, 2519, as is shown in the above illustration.

114

(2) As there are two uprights in the multiplier, the second upright to the right of the multiplicand is the unit upright for the product.

(3) Multiplying the end figure of the multiplicand with the end figure of the multiplier we get, "3×9 is 27."

(4) Raise two Earth counters on the upright for 10's in the product and press between the fingers the Heaven counter and two Earth counters on the unit upright of the product. 251927 should now be indicated on the board.

A

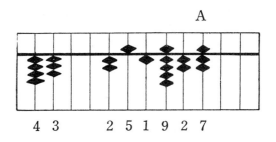

4 3   2 5 1 9 2 7

(5) Multiplying the end figure of the multiplicand by the first figure of the multiplier, we get, "9×4 is 36."

(6) We should now return to place the counters which indicate 9, the end figure of the multiplicand, as we have no further use for it. But we can see that the figure 3 of

115

the product 36 must be indicated on the same upright, so we return to place the Heaven counter and one Earth counter, leaving 3 indicated on the upright for 100's in the product. Then we press between our fingers the Heaven counter and one Earth counter on the next upright to the right, which places our 6 on the upright for 10's in the product. The board should now indicate 251387.

A

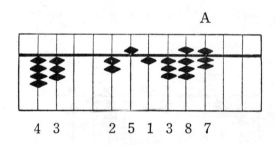

4 3   2 5 1 3 8 7

(7) Multiplying the next figure of the multiplicand with the end figure of the multiplier, we get, "1×3 is 3."

(8) We wish to raise three Earth counters on the upright for 10's in the product, but from the previous multiplication 8 is already indicated on that upright. Therefore, we think, "A. T. 3 and 7 are 10," and we return to place the Heaven

116

counter and two Earth counters on that upright, at the same time raising one Earth counter on the next upright to the left. The board should now indicate 251417.

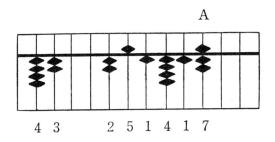

(9) Multiplying this same figure of the multiplicand, 1, by the first figure of the multiplier, we get, "1×4 is 4."

(10) Before indicating this product we must return to place this figure as we have now completed our multiplications. We now want to indicate 4 on the upright for 100's in the product, but there are already four Earth counters in position on that upright, so we think, "A. T. 4 and 1 are 5." We slide down the Heaven counter and at the same time return one Earth counter. The board should now indicate 250817.

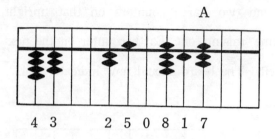

A

4 3   2 5 0 8 1 7

(11) Multiplying the third figure of the multiplicand by the end figure of the multiplier, we get, "3×5 is 15."

(12) Raise one Earth counter on the upright for 1000's in the product. The upright for 100's in the product, on which we wish to indicate 5 has 8 already indicated on it. Therefore, we must think, "A. T. 5 and 5 are 10," and return to place the Heaven counter on that upright, at the same time raising one Earth counter on the next upright to the left.

The board should now indicate 252317.

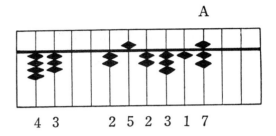

A

4 3   2 5 2 3 1 7

(13) The third figure of the multiplicand multiplied by the first figure of the multiplier gives us, "5×4 is 20."

(14) As we now have no further use for this third figure of the multiplicand we return it to place and then record the multiplication by raising two Earth counters on the upright for 10,000's in the product. 222317 should now be indicated on the board.

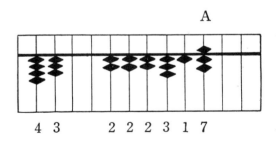

A

4 3   2 2 2 3 1 7

(15) The first figure of the multiplicand multiplied by the end figure of the multiplier gives us, "2×3 is 6."

119

(16) Press between the fingers the Heaven counter and one Earth counter on the upright for 1000's in the product. 228317 should now be indicated on the board.

A

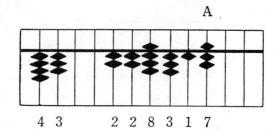

4 3   2 2 8 3 1 7

(17) Multiplying the first figure of the multiplicand by the first figure of the multiplier, we get, " 2×4 is 8."

(18) We have no further use for the figure 2 of the multiplicand, so we return it to place. The upright for 10,000's in the product upon which we wish to record the product 8 has two Earth counters already in position. Therefore, we return these to place and raise one Earth counter on the next upright to the left.

We have now reached the final product. The board should indicate 108317.

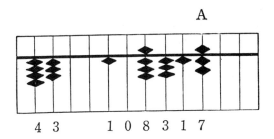

A

4 3   1 0 8 3 1 7

Having completed these exercises we should understand a little of the method of "Multiplication Beginning at the Right." But in case you do not thoroughly understand, I wish to try again to make this method more clear.

When the multiplier is a one place number, the unit position of the product is the next upright to the right of the unit upright of the multiplicand.

We must always decide the unit position of the product first. In long numbers if we find a unit position with each multiplication, the position will advance one upright to the left each time.

I will show you by example what I mean:

A

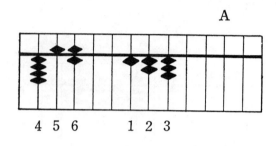

4 5 6   1 2 3

456   multiplier
123   multiplicand
56088   product

As there are three uprights in the multiplier, the third upright to the right of the multiplicand is the unit position of the product.

After indicating our first multiplication, "3×6 is 18", the unit position advances one upright to the left for the next multiplication, "3×5 is 15." Continuing in this way we complete the multiplication.

(1) 3×6 is 18.

①②3   multiplicand
④⑤6   multiplier
  1 8   product

    (6)   (3)   1 8

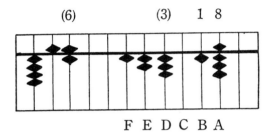

F E D C B A

A upright is the unit position of the product of 3×6.

    (2) 3×5 is 15.

①②3   multiplicand
④5⑥   multiplier
  1 5 0   product

    (5)   (3) 1 5 0

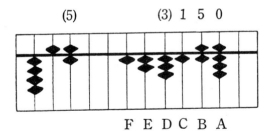

F E D C B A

B upright is the unit position for the product of 3×5.

123

(3) 3×4 is 12.

①② 3 multiplicand
4 ⑤⑥ multiplier
1 2 0 0 product

(3) Return to place

(4)
      1 2 0 0

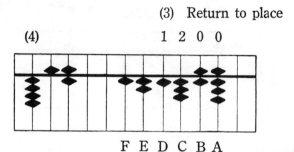

F E D C B A

C upright is the unit position of the product of 3×4.

Thus we have added the (1) and (2) and (3)—18 and 150 and 1200, so 1368 should be indicated on the board.

The figure 3 which is the end figure of the multiplicand has now been multiplied by every figure of the multiplier so it must be returned to place.

(4) 2×6 is 12.

① 2 ③ multiplicand
④⑤ 6 multiplier
1 2 0 product

124

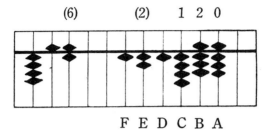

(6)   (2)   1 2 0

F E D C B A

B is the upright for the unit position of the product of 2×6.

Adding the (1) and (2) and (3) and (4) 121488 is indicated on the board.

(5)   2×5 is 10.

①2③   multiplicand
④5⑥   multiplier
‾‾‾‾‾‾‾‾
1 0 0 0   product

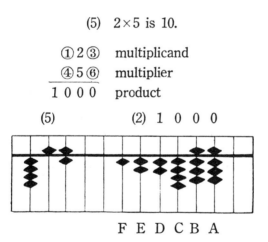

(5)   (2) 1 0 0 0

F E D C B A

C upright is the unit position of the product of 2×5.

Adding the (1) and (2) and (3) and (4) and (5) we get 122488 indicated on the board.

125

(6) 2×4 is 8.

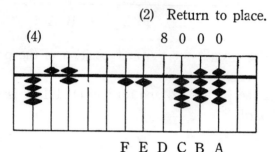

①2③   multiplicand

4⑤⑥   multipiler

8 0 0 0   product

(2)   Return to place.

(4)   8 0 0 0

F E D C B A

D upright is the unit position of the product of 2×4.

Return to place the two Earth counters which indicate the figure 2 of the multiplicand as all multiplications with that figure have been completed.

There are two Earth counters already in position on the upright which is the unit position for our present multiplication; so instead of adding eight to the two think, "2 and 8 are 10". Return to place the two Earth counters and raise one Earth counter on the next upright to the left. Now having added the (1) and (2) and (3) and (4) and (5) and (6) we should have 110488 indicated on the board.

126

(7) 1×6 is 6.

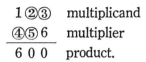

1②③ multiplicand
④⑤6 multiplier
6 0 0 product.

(6)   (1)   6 0 0

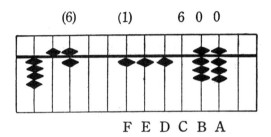

F E D C B A

C is the unit upright for the product of 1×6.

But there are already 4 Earth counters in position on C upright; so thinking, "4 and 6 are 10", replace the four Earth counters and raise one Earth counter on the next upright to the left.

Adding the (1), (2), (3), (4), (5), (6), (7) we should have 111088 indicated on the board.

(8) 1×5 is 5.

1②③ multiplicand
④5⑥ multiplier
5 0 0 0 product

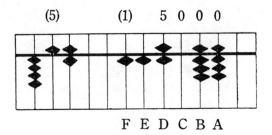

(5)   (1)   5 0 0 0

F E D C B A

D upright is the unit position for the product of 1×5.

Adding the (1), (2), (3), (4), (5), (6), (7), and (8) we have 116088 indicated on the board.

(9) 1×4 is 4.

$$\begin{array}{r} 1②③ \\ 4⑤⑥ \\ \hline 4\,0\,0\,0\,0 \end{array}$$ multiplicand

multiplier

product

(1) Return to place

(4)   4 0 0 0 0

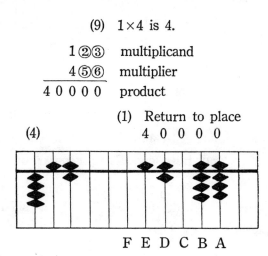

F E D C B A

E upright is the unit position for the product of 1 and 4.

Prior to placing this product on the board we must replace the figure 1 of the Multiplicand as we have no further use for it.

Adding the (1), (2), (3), (4), (5), (6), (7), (8), and (9) we have 56088 on the board.

128

The process of multiplication just completed was as follows :

(1) ① ② 3
   ④ ⑤ 6   3 × 6   18

(2) ① ② 3
   ④ 5 ⑥   3 × 50   150

(3) ① ② 3
   4 ⑤ ⑥   3 × 400   1200

(4) ① 2 ③
   ④ ⑤ 6   20 × 6   120

(5) ① 2 ③
   ④ 5 ⑥   20 × 50   1000

(6) ① 2 ③
   4 ⑤ ⑥   20 × 400   8000

(7) 1 ② ③
   ④ ⑤ 6   100 × 6   600

(8) 1 ② ③
   ④ 5 ⑥   100 × 50   5000

(9) 1 ② ③
   4 ⑤ ⑥   100 × 400   40000
                             56088

A few more illustrations may help to make the process of multiplication clearer.

(1) When we multiply by a number of one place the next upright to the right of the multiplicand becomes the unit upright for the product, as is shown in the following illustration:

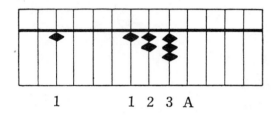

The upright A is the unit position of the product.

(2) When we multiply by a number of two places, the next upright to the right of the multiplicand becomes the position for 10's in the product, as is shown in the following illustration:

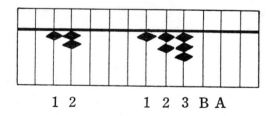

The upright B is the position for 10's in the product, and of course, A is the upright for the unit position.

130

(3) When we multiply by a number of three places, the next upright to the right of the multiplicand is the position for 100's in the product, as is shown in the following illustration:

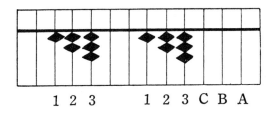

1 2 3   1 2 3 C B A

The upright C is the position for 100's in the product, and, of course, B is for 10's and A is for ones.

These illustrations should be sufficient to make this point clear.

Section 4.

Multiplication Beginning at the Left.

"Multiplication beginning at the Left" is contrary to the method we have just discussed. In this method we begin to multiply with the first figure of the multiplier and the last figure of the multiplicand.

Beginning in this way we can multiply consecutively, so it is easier to handle large numbers by Multiplication Beginning at the Left. Also, it is not so difficult to determine the unit position of the product.

Part 1.

The Process of Multiplication.

(1) Just as in the other method we must indicate the multiplier on the left hand side of the board, and indicate the multiplicand to the right of it.

(2) By the Multiplication Table we multiply the first figure of the multiplier by the last figure of the multiplicand.

(3) Before we indicate this product on the board, we must return to place the counters on the end upright of the multiplicand, which is the position for 10's in the product.

132

(4) Next we multiply the end figure of the multiplicand by the second figure of the multiplier and indicate this product on the second upright to the right of the multiplicand, continuing in this way till we reach the end figure of the multiplier.

Part 2.

The Determination of the Unit Position.

The determination of the Unit position in "Multiplication Beginning at the Left" is very much like the way of determining it in the previous method. Before beginning to multiply we decide that the unit position of the multiplicand is the position for 10's in the product.

If we do this and place the counters each time on the next righthand upright, the last one in the product becomes the unit position.

If we have zeros on the end uprights of both numbers we must count off as many uprights to the right as there are zeros.

I will show you by illustrations.

133

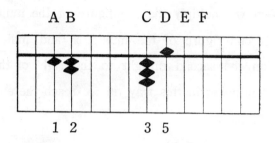

A B   C D E F

1 2   3 5

35   multiplicand

12   multiplier

When we multiply the one on the A upright (the first figure of the multiplier) by the 5 on the D upright (the end figure of the multiplicand), the D upright is the position for 10's and the E upright is the position for ones.

When we multiply the 2 on the B upright by the 5 on the D upright, the E upright is the position for tens in the product, and the F upright is the unit position.

When we multiply the 1 on the A upright by the 3 on the C upright, the C upright is the position for 10's, and the D upright is the unit position.

When we multiply the 2 on the B upright by the 3 on the C upright, the D upright is the position for 10's and the E is the unit position.

134

Part 3.

Example 1.   56   multiplicand
             <u>12</u>   multiplier
            672   product

A

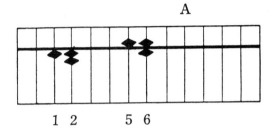

1 2   5 6

A is the unit position of the product.

(1) Place the multiplier on the lefthand side of the board and the multiplicand on the right of it, as is shown in the above illustration.

(2) As there are two uprights in the multiplier, count off two places from the multiplicand and you will find the unit position.

(3) Multiply the 6, which is the end figure of the multiplicand, by the 1, which is the first figure of the multiplier. This gives us, "1×6 is 6."

(4) Before indicating this product we must return to place the figure 6 of the multiplicand and then press between the

fingers the Heaven counter and one Earth counter on the next upright to the right. 5060 should be indicated on the board.

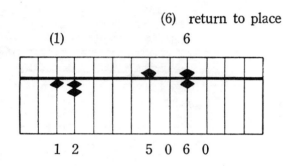

(1)   (6) return to place
                           6

1 2   5 0 6 0

(5) Although we have returned to place the end figure of the multiplicand we must not forget it, as we have not yet completed our multiplications.

(6) We must now multiply the figure 6, which we returned to place, and the second figure of the multiplier. This gives us, "6×2 is 12."

(7) Raise one Earth counter on the next upright to the right, which is the position for 10's in the product, and two Earth counters on the unit upright. 5072 should now be indicated on the board.

136

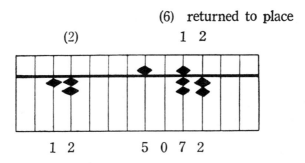

(6) returned to place

(2)   1 2

1 2   5 0 7 2

(8) We have now completed our multiplications with the end figure of the multiplicand, having multiplied it by every figure in the multiplier, beginning with the lefthand figure. We must proceed in this way with each figure of the multiplicand.

(9) Multiplying the second figure of the multiplicand, 5, with the first figure of the multiplier, 1, we get, "5×1 is 5".

(10) Before placing this product we must return to place the figure 5 of the multiplicand. Slide down the 5 counter of the next upright to the right, the position for 100's in the product. 572 should be indicated on the board.

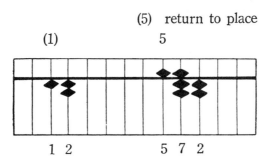

(5) return to place

(1)   5

1 2   5 7 2

137

(11) We must keep in mind that the figure which we returned to place in the multiplicand was 5, as we must now multiply it by the second figure of the multiplier. This gives us, "5×2 is 10."

(12) Raise cne Earth counter on the upright for 100's in the product.

672 is indicated on the board. It is the product.

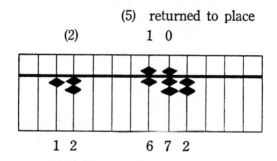

(5)   returned to place

(2)   1   0

1   2   6   7   2

Example 2. 142 multiplicand
           95 multiplier
        13490 product

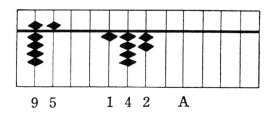

         9 5   1 4 2   A

(1) Indicate the multiplier on the lefthand side of the board and the multiplicand to the right of it, as shown in the above illustration.

(2) As there are two uprights in the multiplier, count off two places to the right of the multiplicand to determine the unit position for the product.

(3) Multiplying the end figure of the multiplicand by the first figure of the multiplier, we get, "2×9 are 18."

(4) Return to place the Earth counters which indicate the figure 2 of the multiplicand. Raise one Earth counter on the same upright to indicate the 10 of the product 18, and on the next upright to the right press between the fingers the 5 counter and three 1 counters, to indicate the 8.

1418 is now indicated on the board.

139

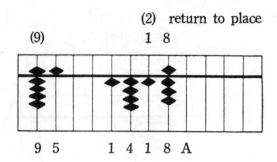

(2) return to place

(9)   1 8

9 5   1 4 1 8 A

(5) We must now multiply the figure 2, which we have returned to place, and the second figure of the multiplier. This gives us, "2×5 is 10."

(6) Raise one Earth counter on the upright for 10's in the product. 1419 should now be indicated on the board.

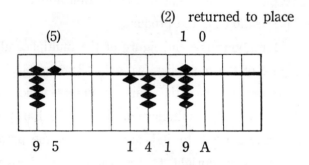

(2) returned to place

(5)   1 0

9 5   1 4 1 9 A

(7) Multiplying the figure 4 of the multiplicand by the first figure of the multiplier, we get, "4×9 is 36."

140

(8) Before placing this product 36, we must return to place the counters which indicate the figure 4 of the multiplicand. Then raise three Earth counters on the same upright and indicate 6 on the next upright to the right. The board should now indicate 13790.

(4)   return to place

(9)   3 6   A

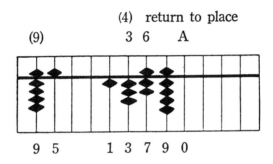

9 5   1 3 7 9 0

(9) Multiplying the figure 4, which we have returned to place, by the second figure of the multiplier, we get, "4×5 is 20."

(10) Raise two Earth counters on the upright for 100's in the product. 13990 should now be indicated on the board.

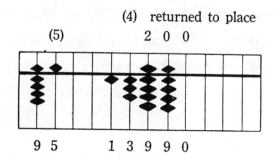

(4) returned to place

(5)   2   0   0

9 5   1 3 9 9 0

(11) Multiplying the figure 1 of the multiplicand by the first figure of the multiplier, we get, "1×9 is 9."

(12) Before placing the product, we must return to place the counter which indicates the figure 1 of the multiplicand. We now wish to indicate the product 9 on the next upright to the right, but from a previous multiplication 3 is already indicated there. Thinking, A. T "9 and 1 are 10", return to place one of these three counters and at the same time raise one Earth counter on the next upright to the left. 12990 is now indicated on the board.

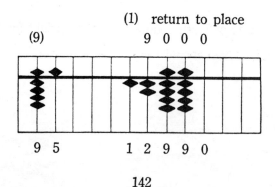

(1) return to place

(9)   9   0   0   0

9 5   1 2 9 9 0

(13) Keeping in mind the figure 1 of the multiplicand, which we have returned to place, we multiply it by the second figure of the multiplier. This gives us, "1×5 is 5."

(14) We now wish to indicate this product on the upright for 100's in the product, but 9 is already indicated there. Therefore, we think, "5 and 5 is 10". And return to place the Heaven counter on that upright and raise one Earth counter on the next upright to the left.

13490 should now be indicated on the board and as we have completed all the multiplications, it is the final product.

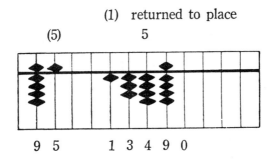

(1) returned to place

(5)　　　　　5

9　5　　　1　3　4　9　0

Example 3.   2854   multiplicand
                  102   multiplier
            ———————
               291108   product

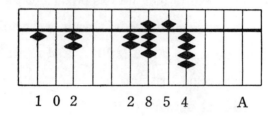

1 0 2   2 8 5 4   A

(1) Indicate the multiplier on the lefthand side of the board and the multiplicand to the right of it as is shown in the above illustration.

(2) As there are three figures in the multiplier, the third upright to the right of the multiplicand is the unit upright for the product.

(3) Multiplying the end figure of the multiplicand by the first figure of the multiplier, we get, "1×4 is 4." Before indicating this product we must return to place the counters which indicate the end figure of the multiplicand and then place our product 4 on the next upright to the right. The board should now indicate 28504.

144

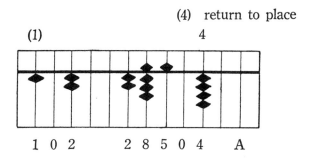

(4)   return to place

(1)   4

1 0 2   2 8 5 0 4   A

(5) Keeping in mind the figure 4 which we have returned to place we multiply it by the end figure of the multiplier. This gives us, "4×2 is 8."

(6) Press between the fingers the Heaven counter and three Earth counters on the unit position of the product. 2850408 should now be indicated on the board.

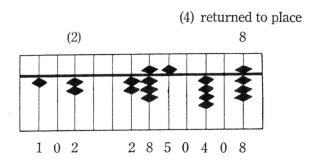

(4) returned to place

(2)   8

1 0 2   2 8 5 0 4 0 8

(7) Multiplying the second figure of the multiplicand with the first figure of the multiplier we get "5×1 is 5."

145

(8) Before indicating this product we must return to place the figure 5 of the multiplicand, then we slide down the Heaven counter on the next upright to the right. 2805408 should now be indicated on the board.

(5) return to place

(1)   5

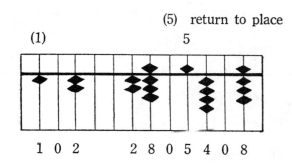

1 0 2   2 8 0 5 4 0 8

(9) Keeping in mind the figure 5 of the multiplicand, which we have returned to place, we multiply it by the end figure of the multiplier, "5×2 is 10."

(10) We wish to indicate this product on the upright for 100's in the product but as there are already four Earth counters in position on that upright we slide down the Heaven counter and return the four Earth counters. 2805508 should now be indicated on the board.

146

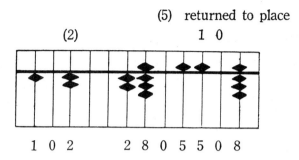

(5) returned to place

(2)   1 0

1 0 2   2 8 0 5 5 0 8

(11) Multiplying the third figure of the multiplicand by the first figure of the multiplier we get, "8×1 is 8."

(12) Before indicating this product we return to place the counters representing the figure 8 of the multiplicand, then we indicate the product 8 on the next upright to the right. 2085508 should now be indicated on the board.

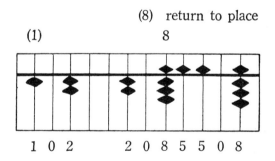

(8) return to place

(1)   8

1 0 2   2 0 8 5 5 0 8

(13) Keeping in mind the figure 8 which we have returned to place multiply it by the last figure of the multiplier. This gives us, "8×2 is 16."

147

(14) Raise one Earth counter on the upright for 1000's in the prcduct. This indicates the 10 of our product 16. On the next upright to the right where we wish to indicate the 6 there is 5 already indicated from a previous multiplication. Therefore we must think, "5 and 5 are 10", and raising one Earth counter on the 100 upright, return the Heaven counter on the 100 upright to place and raise one Earth counter on the next upright to the left. 2087108 should now be indicated on the board.

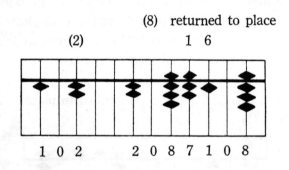

(8) returned to place

(2)   1   6

1 0 2   2 0 8 7 1 0 8

(15) Multiplying the first figure of the multiplicand by the first figure of the multiplier we get, "2×1 is 2."

(16) Return to place the counters which are used to indicate the figure 2 of the multiplicand, and raise two Earth counters on the next upright to the right. 287108 should be indicated on the board.

148

(17) Keeping in mind the figure 2 of the multiplicand we multiply it by the last figure of the multiplier. This gives us, "2×2 is 4."

(18) We wish to indicate this product on the upright for 1000's in the product but as it already indicates 7 we think, "4 and 6 are 10" and return to place the Heaven counter and one Earth counter on the upright, at the same time raising one Earth counter on the next upright to the left.

291108 is indicated and it is the final product.

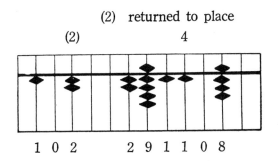

(2) returned to place

(2)   4

1 0 2   2 9 1 1 0 8

Cover the product in row A. Multiply and write the products. Compare your results with the printed products.

Do again any which were wrong. Do the same with row B and the other rows.

Row A.

Multiplicand	316	423	265
Multiplier	24	19	27
Product	7584	8037	7155

Row B.

Multiplicand	95	127	328
Multiplier	76	56	234
Product	7220	7112	76752

Row C.

Multiplicand	29	103	235
Multiplier	14	54	25
Product	406	5562	5875

Row D.

Multiplicand	$ 7.24	$ 8.06
Multiplier	86	92
Product	$ 622.64	$ 741.52

Row E.

Multiplicand	$ 64.76	$ 76.32
Multiplier	84	89
Product	$ 5439.84	$ 6792.48

150

Section 5.

Multiplying with Decimals.

There is no difference in the process of multiplication for decimals and ordinary numbers. The only difference is in determining the unit position.

(1) When the multiplier has no zero directly below the decimal point, we consider the unit position of the multiplicand, the unit position for the product.

(2) When the multiplier has two zeros below the decimal point, we count off two places from the unit position of the multiplicand to the left. This is the unit position of the product.

Some illustrations will make this point clear.

Example 1.

2345   multiplicand

0.123   multiplier

The upright A is the unit position of the product.

A

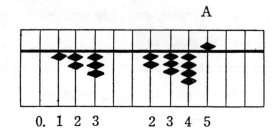

0. 1 2 3   2 3 4 5

Example 2.

2345   multiplicand

0.00123   multiplier

The upright A is the unit position for the product.

A

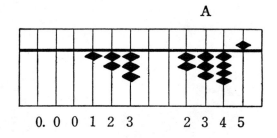

0. 0 0 1 2 3   2 3 4 5

152

Section 6.

Multiplying Tenths and Hundredths.

You can multiply with decimals, which includes numbers that represent dollars and cents, just as you multiply integers, if you put the decimal point where it belongs in the product.

$$23.45 \times 52 =$$

After you have multiplied with the decimals just as you would with whole numbers, point off as many decimal places in the product as there are in the multiplier and the multiplicand together.

Find the product.

Row A.

(1) $138 \times 2 =$

(2) $243 \times 3 =$

(3) $358 \times 4 =$

(4) $519 \times 5 =$

(5) $472 \times 6 =$

Row B.

(1) $682 \times 6 =$

(2) $737 \times 7 =$

(3) $685 \times 8 =$

(4) $946 \times 9 =$

(5) $478 \times 2 =$

Cover the answer with a card. State each product. Then look at the answer to make sure that you were right.

(1)	$604 \times 39 = 23556$		(16)	$\$2.63 \times 47 = \$123.61$
(2)	$746 \times 41 = 30586$		(17)	$\$5.03 \times 42 = \$211.26$
(3)	$824 \times 48 = 39552$		(18)	$\$9.25 \times 38 = \$351.50$
(4)	$983 \times 52 = 51116$		(19)	$\$6.74 \times 81 = \$545.94$
(5)	$198 \times 57 = 11286$		(20)	$\$3.27 \times 29 = \$94.83$
(6)	$217 \times 64 = 13888$		(21)	$\$5.54 \times 48 = \$265.92$
(7)	$362 \times 65 = 23530$		(22)	$\$1.32 \times 56 = \$73.92$
(8)	$439 \times 73 = 32047$		(23)	$\$2.25 \times 47 = \$105.75$
(9)	$573 \times 79 = 45267$		(24)	$\$4.55 \times 32 = \$145.60$
(10)	$661 \times 81 = 53541$		(25)	$\$4.01 \times 58 = \$232.58$
(11)	$724 \times 86 = 62264$		(26)	$\$5.83 \times 49 = \$285.67$
(12)	$806 \times 92 = 74152$		(27)	$\$7.11 \times 31 = \$220.41$
(13)	$955 \times 98 = 93590$		(28)	$\$8.25 \times 53 = \$437.25$
(14)	$1647 \times 13 = 21411$		(29)	$\$9.03 \times 12 = \$108.36$
(15)	$2838 \times 16 = 45408$		(30)	$\$3.42 \times 48 = \$164.16$

CHAPTER V.

DIVISION

There are two methods of division in general use, " Division by Unification ", and " Division by Abbreviation."

Division by Unification.

In this method both Division and Multiplication Tables are used.

Division by Abbreviation.

In this method only Multiplication Table is used in solving the problems.

$$\begin{array}{r} 44 \quad \text{quotient} \\ \text{Divisor} \quad 28\overline{)1232} \quad \text{dividend} \end{array}$$

Section 1.

Division by Unification.

This is the method in which we use both Multiplication and Division Tables when we divide the dividend by the divisor.

By this method we can find out on the abacus how many times a certain number is contained in another number.

If you memorize the Division Table you will find this new method of division more simple than division in writing.

Part 1.

Division Table by Unification.

Dividing by 1.

1 into 1 advance 1				1 into 6 advance 6			
1 " 2 " 2				1 " 7 " 7			
1 " 3 " 3				1 " 8 " 8			
1 " 4 " 4				1 " 9 " 9			
1 " 5 " 5							

Illustration of Division by 1.

$$\text{Divisor } 1 \overline{)\,6\,}^{\,6\text{ quotient}}_{\text{ dividend}}$$

A

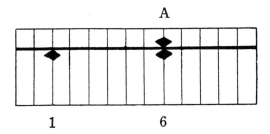

1   6

Dividing the 6 on the A upright by the 1, we get, "1 into 6 advance 6." We return to place the counters which indicate 6 and on the next upright to the left indicate the quotient 6.

The entire Division Table of 1 is done in this way, advancing one upright to the left for the quotient.

Dividing by 2.

2	into	1	Heaven	5
2	into	2	advance	1

Illustrations of Division by 2.

$$\text{Divisor} \quad 2\overline{)\;1\;}\quad \begin{matrix}.5 \quad \text{quotient}\\ \text{dividend}\end{matrix}$$

A

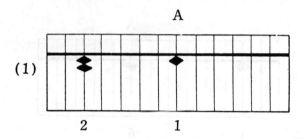

(1)

2   1

When we divide the 1 on the A upright by 2, we get, "2 into 1 Heaven 5." Return to place the Earth counter on the A upright and slide down the Heaven counter on the same upright. This indicates .5 on the board.

$$\text{Divisor} \quad 2\overline{)\;2\;}\quad \begin{matrix}1 \quad \text{quotient}\\ \text{dividend}\end{matrix}$$

B A

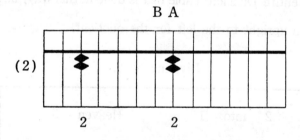

(2)

2   2

Dividing the 2 on the A upright by 2, we get, "2 into 2 advance 1."

158

Return to place the two Earth counters on the A upright and at the same time raise one Earth counter on the next upright to the left.

The quotient 1 is now indicated on the board.

Dividing by 3.

3 into 1	3 and 1 over
3 into 2	6 and 2 over
3 into 3	advance 1

Illustrations of Division by 3.

3 into 1   3 and 1 over

$$\text{Divisor} \quad 3\overline{)\,1\,} \quad \begin{array}{l}\text{3 and 1 over} \quad \text{quotient}\\ \text{dividend}\end{array}$$

A B

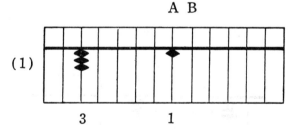

(1)

3   1

When we divide the 1 on the A upright by 3, we get, "3 into 1, 3 and 1 over." Instead of returning to place the Earth counter on the A upright, add two counters to it and raise one Earth counter on the next upright to the right, the B upright.

159

31 is indicated on the board.

$$\begin{array}{r} 6 \text{ and } 2 \text{ over} \quad \text{quotient} \\ \text{Divisor} \quad 3\overline{)\ 2} \quad \text{dividend} \end{array}$$

A B

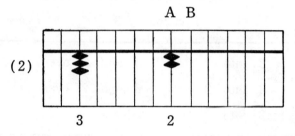

When we divide the 2 on the A upright by 3, we get, "3 into 2, 6 and 2 over." Instead of returning to place the two Earth counters on the A upright, add four Earth counters to them and raise two Earth counters on the B upright, which is the next upright to the right.

62 is indicated on the board.

$$\begin{array}{r} 1 \quad \text{quotient} \\ \text{Divisor} \quad 3\overline{)\ 3} \quad \text{dividend} \end{array}$$

B A

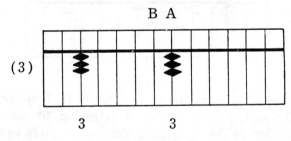

When we divide the 3 on the A upright by 3, we get, "3 into 3 advance 1."

160

Return to place the three Earth counters on the A upright, and at the same time raise one Earth counter on the next upright to the left, or the B upright.

1 is indicated on the board.

Dividing by 4.

4 into 1	2 and 2 over
4 into 2	Heaven 5
4 into 3	7 and 2 over
4 into 4	advance 1

Illustrations of Division by 4.

$$\frac{2 \text{ and } 2 \text{ over}}{4)\,1} \quad \text{quotient}$$

Divisor 4) 1 dividend

A B

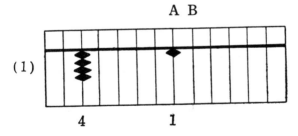

(1)

4   1

When we divide the 1 on the A upright by 4, we get, "4 into 1, 2 and 2 over." Instead of returning to place the 1 Earth counter on the A upright, add one Earth counter to it, then raise two Earth counters on the B upright, which is the next upright to the right.

22 is indicated on the board.

$$\frac{5}{4)\ 2}\quad\begin{array}{l}\text{quotient}\\\text{dividend}\end{array}$$

Divisor

A

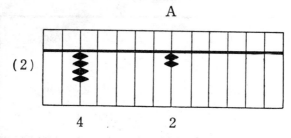

(2)

4   2

When we divide the 2 on the A upright by 4, we get, "4 into 2 Heaven 5." Return to place the Earth counters which are on the A upright and then slide down the Heaven counter, which is on the same upright.

5 is indicated on the board.

$$\frac{7 \text{ and } 2 \text{ over}}{4)\ 3}\quad\begin{array}{l}\text{quotient}\\\text{dividend}\end{array}$$

Divisor

A B

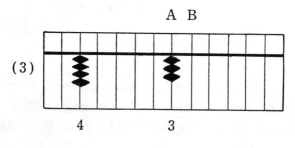

(3)

4   3

162

When we divide the 3 on the A upright by 4, we get, "4 into 3, 7 and 2 over." Instead of returning to place the 3 Earth counters on the A upright, add 4 Earth counters to this upright and raise two Earth counters on the next upright to the right, or the B upright.

72 is indicated on the board.

$$\frac{1}{4)\ 4}\ \begin{array}{l}\text{quotient}\\ \text{dividend}\end{array}$$

Divisor

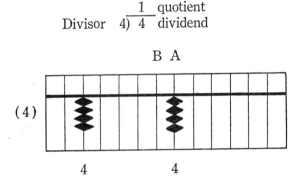

B A

(4)

4   4

When we divide the 4 on the A upright by 4, we get, "4 into 4, advance 1." Return to place the four Earth counters on the A upright and raise one Earth counter on the next upright to the left, or the B upright.

1 is indicated on the board.

163

Dividing by 5.

5	into	1	plus	1
5	into	2	plus	2
5	into	3	plus	3
5	into	4	plus	4
5	into	5	advance	1

Illustrations of Division by 5.

$$\text{Divisor} \quad 5)\overline{\begin{array}{l}2 \\ 1\end{array}}\begin{array}{l}\text{quotient} \\ \text{dividend}\end{array}$$

A

(1)

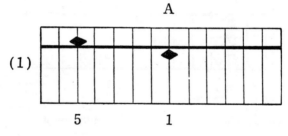

5   1

When we divide the 1 on the A upright by 5, we get, "5 into 1, plus 1." Add the 1 to the 1 Earth counter on the A upright.

2 is indicated on the board.

$$\text{Divisor} \quad 5)\overline{\begin{array}{l}4 \\ 2\end{array}}\begin{array}{l}\text{quotient} \\ \text{dividend}\end{array}$$

164

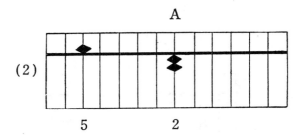

A

(2)

5   2

When we divide the 2 on the A upright by 5, we get, "5 into 2, plus 2." Add the 2 to the two Earth counters on the A upright.

4 is indicated on the board.

$$\begin{array}{r} 6 \\ \hline \end{array}\ \text{quotient}$$

Divisor 5) 3 dividend

A

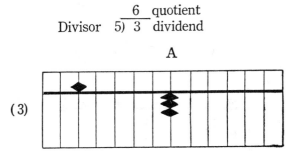

(3)

5   3

When we divide the 3 on the A upright by 5, we get, "5 into 3, plus 3." Add the 3 Earth counters on the A upright where 3 is already indicated.

6 is indicated on the board.

165

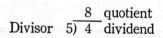

$$\text{Divisor} \quad 5\overline{)\,4} \quad \frac{8}{} \quad \begin{array}{l}\text{quotient}\\ \text{dividend}\end{array}$$

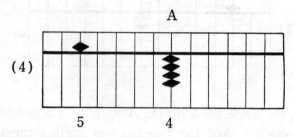

When we divide the 4 on the A upright by 5, we get, "5 into 4, plus 4." Add 4 Earth counters to the 4 already indicated on the A upright.

8 is indicated on the board.

$$\text{Divisor} \quad 5\overline{)\,5} \quad \frac{1}{} \quad \begin{array}{l}\text{quotient}\\ \text{dividend}\end{array}$$

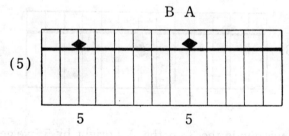

When we divide the 5 on the A upright by 5, we get, "5 into 5, advance 1." Return to place the Heaven counter on the A upright and raise one Earth counter on the next upright to the left, or the B upright.

1 is indicated on the board.

Dividing by 6.

6	into	1	1	and	4	over
6	into	2	3	and	2	over
6	into	3	Heaven	5		
6	into	4	6	and	4	over
6	into	5	8	and	2	over
6	into	6	advance	1		

Illustrations of Division by 6.

1 and 4 over   quotient
Divisor 6) 1 dividend

A B

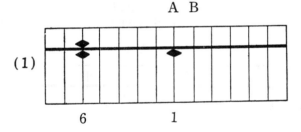

(1)

6   1

When we divide the 1 on the A upright by 6, we get, " 6 into 1, 1 and 4 over." Raise 4 Earth counters on the next upright to the right, or the B upright.

14 is indicated on the board.

3 and 2 over   quotient
Divisor 6) 2 dividend

167

A B

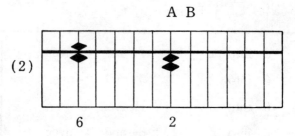

(2)

6　　　　　2

When we divide the 2 on the A upright by 6, we get, "6 into 2, 3 and 2 over." Instead of returning to place the two Earth counters on the A upright, add one Earth counter to them and raise two Earth counters on the next upright to the right, or the B upright.

32 is indicated on the board.

$$\begin{array}{r} 5 \quad \text{quotient} \\ \text{Divisor} \quad 6) \overline{ 3} \quad \text{dividend} \end{array}$$

A

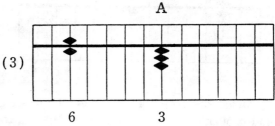

(3)

6　　　　　3

When we divide the 3 on the A upright by 6, we get, "6 into 3 Heaven 5." Return to place the three Earth counters cn the A upright, and at the same time, slide down the Heaven counter on the same upright.

168

5 is indicated on the board.

```
                6 and 4 over   quotient
    Divisor   6) 4  dividend
```

A B

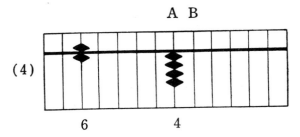

(4)

6   4

When we divide 4 by 6, we get, "6 into 4, 6 and 4 over." Instead of returning to place the four counters which are indicated on the A upright, add two Earth counters to this upright. Then raise four Earth counters on the next upriht to the right, the B upright.

64 is indicated on the board.

```
                8 and 2 over   quotient
    Divisor   6) 5  dividend
```

A B

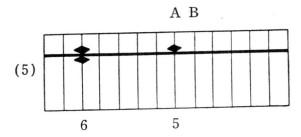

(5)

6   5

When we divide 5 on the A upright by 6, we get, "6 into 5, 8 and 2 over." Instead of returning to place the

169

Heaven counter on the A upright, add three Earth counters
to it and then raise two Earth counters on the next upright
to the right.

82 is indicated on the board.

$$\frac{1}{\text{Divisor} \quad 6)\ 6} \text{ quotient}$$
$$\text{dividend}$$

B A

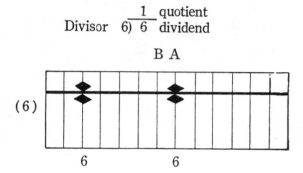

(6)

      6   6

When we divide the 6 on the A upright by 6, we get, "6
into 6 advance 1." We return to place the counters which
indicate 6 on the A upright and raise one Earth counter
on the next upright to the left.

1 is indicated on the board.

Dividing by 7.

7	into	1	1	and	3 over
7	into	2	2	and	6 over
7	into	3	4	and	2 over
7	into	4	5	and	5 over
7	into	5	7	and	1 over
7	into	6	8	and	4 over
7	into	7	advance	1	

Illustrations of Division by 7.

                    1 and 3 over   quotient
        Divisor   7) 1   dividend

                    A B

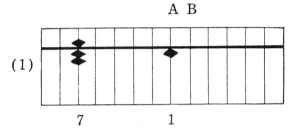

(1)

        7   1

When we divide the 1 on the A upright by 7, we get,
"7 into 1, 1 and 3 over." We raise three Earth counters
on the next upright to the right of the A upright.

13 is indicated on the board.

                    2 and 6 over   quotient
        Divisor   7) 2   dividend

                    A B

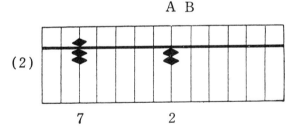

(2)

        7   2

When we divide the 2 on the A upright by 7, we get, "7
into 2, 2 and 6 over." We raise 6 on the next upright to
the right of the A upright.

171

26 is indicated on the board.

<pre>
                4 and 2 over   quotient
Divisor   7) 3   dividend
</pre>

A B

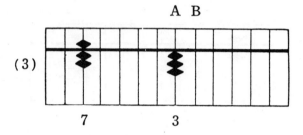

(3)

7   3

When we divide the three on the A upright by 7, we get, "7 into 3, 4 and 2 over." Instead of returning to place the three Earth counters on the A upright, add one Earth counter to these. Then raise two Earth counters on the next upright to the right, or the B upright.

42 is indicated on the board.

<pre>
                5 and 5 over   quotient
Divisor   7) 4   dividend
</pre>

A B

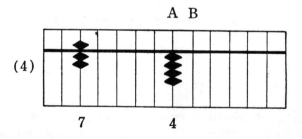

(4)

7   4

When we divide the 4 on the A upright by 7, we get, "7

172

into 4, 5 and 5 over." Instead of returning to place the four Earth counters on the A upright add one Earth counter to these and then slide down the Heaven counter on the next upright to the right, or the B upright.

55 is indicated on the board.

$$\begin{array}{r} 7 \text{ and } 1 \text{ over} \quad \text{quotient} \\ \text{Divisor} \quad 7\overline{)\ 5} \quad \text{dividend} \end{array}$$

A B

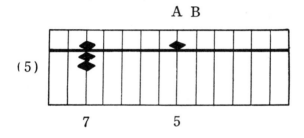

(5)

7   5

When we divide the 5 on the A upright by 7, we get, " 7 into 5, 7 and 1 over." Instead of returning to place the Heaven counter on the A upright, add two Earth counters to it and then raise one Earth counter on the next upright to the right.

71 is indicated on the board.

$$\begin{array}{r} 8 \text{ and } 4 \text{ over} \quad \text{quotient} \\ \text{Divisor} \quad 7\overline{)\ 6} \quad \text{dividend} \end{array}$$

173

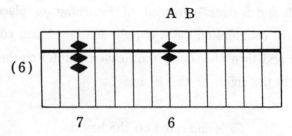

(6)

7   6

When we divide the 6 on the A upright by 7, we get, " 7 into 6, 8 and 4 over." Instead of returning to place the counters which indicate 6 on the A upright, add two Earth counters to these and then raise four Earth counters on the next upright to the right, or the B upright.

84 is indicated on the board.

$$\text{Divisor} \quad 7\overline{)\, 7} \quad \begin{array}{l} 1 \text{ quotient} \\ \text{dividend} \end{array}$$

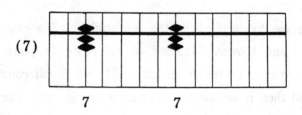

(7)

7   7

When we divide the 7 on the A upright by 7, we get, " 7 into 7, advance 1." Return to place the counters which indicate 7 on the A upright and then raise one Earth counter on the next upright to the left.

1 is indicated on the board.

174

Dividing by 8.

8	into	1	1	and	2	over
8	into	2	2	and	4	over
8	into	3	3	and	6	over
8	into	4	Heaven	5		
8	into	5	6	and	2	over
8	into	6	7	and	4	over
8	into	7	8	and	6	over
8	into	8	advance	1		

Illustrations of Division by 8.

$$\frac{1 \text{ and } 2 \text{ over}}{\text{Divisor} \quad 8)\ \overline{1}} \quad \text{quotient} \atop \text{dividend}$$

A B

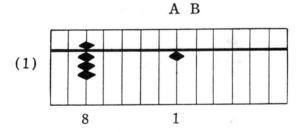

(1)

8   1

When we divide the 1 on the A upright by 8, we get, "8 into 1, 1 and 2 over." We raise two Earth counters on the next upright to the right of the A upright, or the B upright.

12 is indicated on the board.

175

$$\frac{\text{2 and 4 over}}{\text{Divisor } 8)\ \overline{2}\ \text{dividend}} \quad \text{quotient}$$

A B

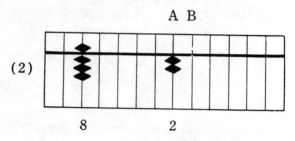

(2)

8   2

When we divide the 2 on the A upright by 8, we get, " 8 into 2, 2 and 4 over." Raise four Earth counters on the next upright to the right of the A upright, or the B upright.

24 is indicated on the board.

$$\frac{\text{3 and 6 over}}{\text{Divisor } 8)\ \overline{3}\ \text{dividend}} \quad \text{quotient}$$

A B

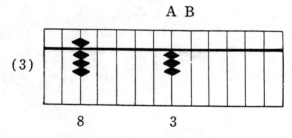

(3)

8   3

When we divide the 3 on the A upright by 8, we get, " 8 into 3, 3 and 6 over." We indicate 6 on the next upright to theright of the A upright, or the B upright.

36 is indicated on the board.

$$\frac{5}{8)\ \overline{4}}\ \text{quotient}$$

Divisor is 8), dividend is 4

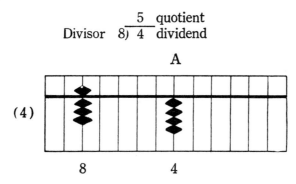

A

(4)

8   4

When we divide the 4 on the A upright by 8, we get, "8 into 4, Heaven 5." Return to place the four Earth counters on the A upright and slide down the Heaven counter on the same upright.

5 is indicated on the board.

6 and 2 over quotient
Divisor   8) 5   dividend

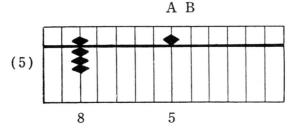

A B

(5)

8   5

When we divide the 5 on the A upright by 8, we get, "8 into 5, 6 and 2 over." Instead of returning to place the Heaven counter on the A upright, add one Earth counter to it and raise two Earth counters on the next upright to the right, or the B upright.

177

62 is indicated on the board.

```
                7 and 4 over quotient
Divisor   8) 6   dividend
```

A B

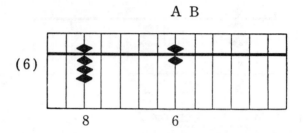

When we divide the 6 on the A upright by 8, we get, "8 into 6, 7 and 4 over." Instead of returning to place the counters which indicate 6 on the A upright, add one Earth counter to them and then raise four Earth counters on the next upright to the right, or the B upright.

74 is indicated on the board.

```
                8 and 6 over quotient
Divisor   8) 7   dividend
```

A B

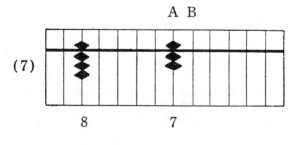

When we divide the 7 on the A upright by 8, we get, "8 into 7, 8 and 6 over." Instead of returning to place the counters which indicate 7 on the A upright, add one Earth counter to them and on the next upright to the right, indicate 6.

86 is indicated on the board.

$$\frac{1}{8)\ 8}\ \begin{array}{l}\text{quotient}\\\text{dividend}\end{array}$$

Divisor

B A

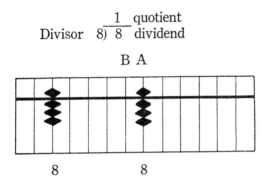

8   8

When we divide the 8 on the A upright by 8, we get, "8 into 8, advance 1." Return to place the counters which indicate 8 on the A upright, and raise one Earth counter on the next upright to the left.

1 is indicated on the board.

Dividing by 9.

9	into	1	1 and	1	over
9	into	2	2 and	2	over
9	into	3	3 and	3	over
9	into	4	4 and	4	over
9	into	5	5 and	5	over
9	into	6	6 and	6	over
9	into	7	7 and	7	over
9	into	8	8 and	8	over
9	into	9	advance 1		

Illustrations of Division by 9.

$$\begin{array}{r} \text{1 and 1 over quotient} \\ \text{Divisor} \quad 9 \overline{)\ 1\ } \ \text{divipend} \end{array}$$

A B

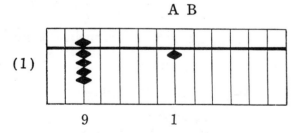

(1)

     9   1

When we divide the 1 on the A upright by 9, we get, "9 into 1, 1 and 1 over." Raise one Earth counter on the next upright to the right, or the B upright.

180

11 is indicated on the board.

9 into 1 through 9 into 8 are solved by the same method.

$$\frac{1}{9)\ 9}\ \begin{array}{l}\text{quotient}\\ \end{array}$$

Divisor 9) 9 dividend

B A

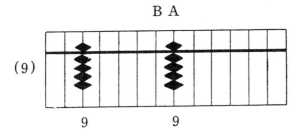

(9)

    9   9

When we divide the 9 on the A upright by 9, we get, "9 into 9, advance 1." Return to place the counters which indicate 9 on the A upright and raise one Earth counter on the next upright to the left, or the B upright.

1 is indicated on the board.

Practical Application of the Divison Table.

2	into	4	advance	2
2	into	6	advance	3
2	into	8	advance	4
3	into	6	advance	2
3	into	9	advance	3
4	into	8	advance	2

These division tables should not be difficult to learn by heart.

Long division in writing is complicated and difficult to do accurately, but if you learn the Division Tables, long division is very simple on the abacus, because it is accomplished by dividing the figures on each upright one by one, and therefore, the figures are always between 1 and 9.

Practical Use of the Tables in " Division by Unification."

Memorization of the tables is absolutely necessary before trying to divide by this method.

If the first figure of the divisor is 1, we use the table for dividing by 1. If the first figure of the divisor is 2 we use the table for dividing by 2.

The following example will show how to proceed by this method.

Example 1.

In this case the first figure of the dividend is larger than the first figure of the divisor.

$$\frac{3}{13)\overline{39}} \begin{array}{l} \text{quotient} \\ \text{dividend} \end{array}$$

Divisor

A B C

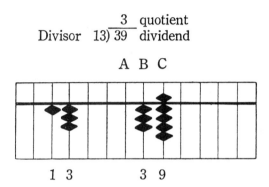

1 3 3 9

As the first figure of the divisor is 1, we must use the table for dividing by 1.

(1) Dividing the 3, which is the first figure of the dividend, by the 1, which is the first figure of the divisor, we get, "1 into 3 advance 3." Return to place the three Earth Counters on the first upright of the dividend and raise 3 Earth counters on the next upright to the left, in this case the A upright. 309 should be indicated on the board.

A B C

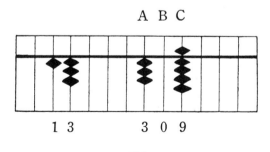

1 3 3 0 9

183

Now we multiply the 3 of the temporary quotient on the A upright by the 3 which is the second figure of the divisor. This gives us, "3×3 are 9." We then return to place the counters which indicate 9 on the last upright of the dividend.

3 is indicated on the board, and it is the quotient.

Example 2.

In this case, the first figure of the dividend is smaller than the first figure of the divisor.

$$\frac{6}{\text{Divisor } 26) \overline{156}} \begin{array}{l} \text{quotient} \\ \text{dividend} \end{array}$$

A B C

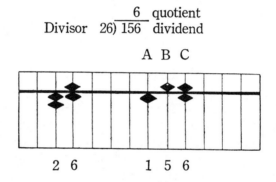

2 6   1 5 6

As the first figure of the divisor is 2, we must use the table for dividing by 2.

(1) Dividing the 1, which is the first figure of the dividend, by the 2, which is the first figure of the divisor, we get, "2 into 1 Heaven 5." Return to place the Earth counter on the first upright of the dividend, and then slide down the Heaven counter on the same upright. 556 should now be indicated on the board.

A B C

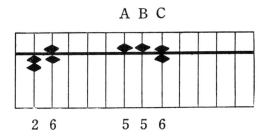

2 6   5 5 6

(2) Dividing the 5, which is the second figure of the dividend, by the 2, which is the first figure of the divisor, we get, "2 into 2 advance 1." (explained later.) Return to place the two Earth counters on the upright for tens in the dividend, and raise one Earth counter on the next upright to the left. As there is already a Heaven counter in place on that upright, we now have 6 there, and the board should indicate 636.

A B C

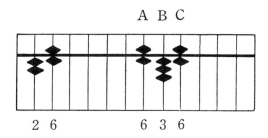

2 6   6 3 6

(3) Multiplying the 6 of the temporary quotient, which is on the A upright by the 6 on the end upright of the divisor,

185

we get, "6×6 are 36." We return to place the three Earth counters on the upright for tens and the counters which indicate 6 on the end upright of the dividend.

6 is indicated on the board. It is the quotient.

Please note: in spite of the fact that when we divide the 5 on the upright for tens by 2, we get 2 in the temporary quotient, we say, "2 into 2 advance 1." Otherwise, we would get into trouble, for if we said, "2 into 4 advance 2", and we indicated 2 on the first upright of the dividend, 716 would be indicated on the board.

A B C

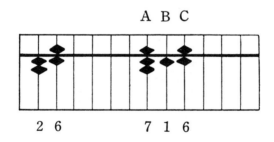

2 6   7 1 6

Then multiplying the 7 of the temporary quotient on the A upright of the dividend by the 6 on the end upright of the divisor, we would get, "6×7 are 42." But we could not subtract 42 from 16. Therefore, we must use, "2 into 2 advance 1."

Example 3.

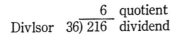

$$\frac{6}{36 \overline{)\, 216}} \quad \text{quotient}$$

Divlsor   36) 216   dividend

A B C

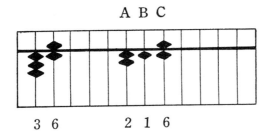

3 6   2 1 6

As the first figure of the divisor is 3, we must use the table for divididg by 3.

(1) Dividing the 2 on the first upright of the dividend by the 3 on the first upright of the divisor, we get, "3 into 2 6 and 2 over." Instead of returning to place the 2 Earth counters on the first upright of the dividend, add 4 to this same upright and raise two Earth counters on the next upright to the right, or the B upright. 636 should be indicated on the board.

A B C

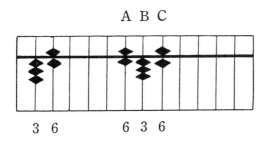

3 6   6 3 6

187

Multiplying the 6 of the temporary quotient on the first upright of the dividend, by the 6 on the last upright of the divisor, we get, "6×6 are 36." Return to place the three Earth counters on the upright for tens in the dividend and the 6 on the last upright of the dividend.

6 is indicated on the board. It is the quotient.

Example 4.

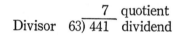

Divisor 63) 441 dividend
with 7 quotient

A B C

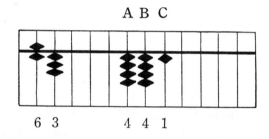

6 3   4 4 1

As the first figure of the divisor is 6, we must use the table for dividing by 6.

(1) Dividing the 4 on the first upright of the dividend by the 6 on the first upright of the divisor, we get, " 6 into 4 6 and 4 over." Instead of returning to place the 4 Earth counters on the first upright of the dividend, add two to the same upright, and raise four Earth counters on the next upright to the right, or the B upright. 681 should be indicated on the board.

188

A B C

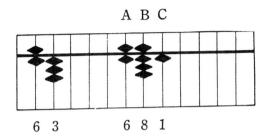

6 3   6 8 1

(2) Dividing the 8 on the B upright by 6, we get, " 6 into 6 advance 1." We return to place the counters which indicate 6 of the 8 indicated on the B upright, and then raise one Earth counter on the next upright to the left. 721 should be indicated on the board.

A B C

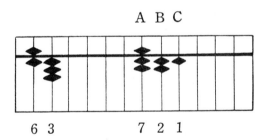

6 3   7 2 1

(3) Multiplying the 7 of the temporary quotient on the first upright of the dividend and the 3 on the last upright of the divisor, we get, "3×7 are 21." Return to place the two Earth counters on the upright for tens in the dividend and one Earth counter on the unit upright.

7 is indicated on the board. It is the quotient.

189

Example 5.

$$\frac{5}{53) \overline{265}} \quad \begin{array}{l} \text{quotient} \\ \text{dividend} \end{array}$$

Divisor

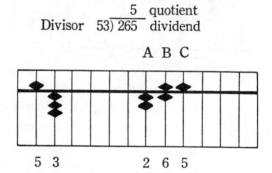

A B C

5 3   2 6 5

As the first figure of the divisor is 5, we must use the table for dividing by 5.

(1) Dividing the 2, which is the first figure of the dividend, by 5, on the first upright of the divisor, we get, "5 into 2 plus 2." Raise two Earth counters on the first upright of the dividend. 465 should be indicated on the board.

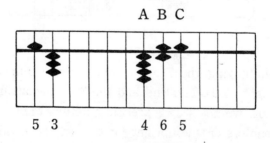

A B C

5 3   4 6 5

(2) Dividing the 6 on the B upright of the dividend by the 5 on the first upright of the divisor, we get, "5 into 5 advance 1." Return to place the Heaven counter on the B

upright of the dividend and raise one Earth counter on the next upright to the left, or the A upright. 515 should be indicated on the board.

A B C

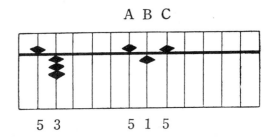

5 3　　5 1 5

(3) Multiplying the 5 of the temporary quotient on the first upright of the dividend and the 3 on the last upright of the divisor, we get, "3×5 are 15." Return to place the Earth counter on the upright for tens in the dividend and the Heaven counter on the unit upright.

5 is indicated on the board. It is the quotient.

Example 6.

$$\frac{8}{92)\,736} \begin{array}{l} \text{quotient} \\ \text{dividend} \end{array}$$
Divisor

A B C

9 2　　7 3 6

As the first figure of the divisor is 9, we must use the table for dividing by 9.

(1) Dividing the 7 on the first upright of the dividend by the 9 on the first upright of the divisor, we get, "9 into 7, 7 and 7 over." We then wish to put 7 on the B upright, but there are already three Earth counters in position there. If we add the 7 to the 3, the upright for tens will be full, therefore, we must divide the 10 by the 9 on the first upright of the divisor. This gives us, "9 into 9 advance 1." Instead of adding the 7 to the 3 on the upright for tens of the dividend, we return to place the two Earth counters on the same upright. Raise one Earth counter on the next upright to the left, or the A upright.

816 should be indicated on the board.

A B C

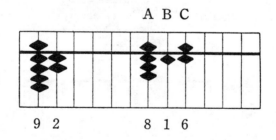

9 2　　8 1 6

(2) Multiplying the 8 of the temporary quotient on the first upright of the dividend and the 2 on the last upright of the divisor, we get, "2×8 are 16." Return to place the Earth counter on the upright for tens in the dividend and the counters, which indicate 6 on the unit upright.

8 is indicated on the board. It is the quotient.

Please note that sometimes in the process of division an upright will become full as it did in the previous example, or you may have more than 10 to indicate on one upright. In such cases we must think how much we should add to the number in order to make it the same as the divisor, and then subtract that number from the lower upright and raise one Earth counter on the next upright to the left, as is shown in the following illustration.

$$\frac{696}{7)\,4872}\begin{array}{l}\text{quotient}\\\text{dividend}\end{array}$$

Divisor

A B C D

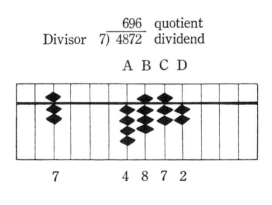

7   4 8 7 2

Dividing the 4 on the first upright of the dividend by the divisor, we get, "7 into 4, 5 and 5 over." Slide down the Heaven counter on the first upright of the dividend and return to place the four Earth counters on the same upright and add 5 on the next upright to the right. But there are already counters indicating 8 on that upright, and if we add 5 to it, there would be more than 10. Therefore, we keep the 5 in mind. 5872 would be indicated on the board, but with the 5 in our minds it would mean 5 (13) 72.

5 (carried in mind)

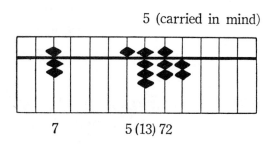

7   5 (13) 72

(2) Dividing the 13 on the upright for hundreds by the divisor, we get, "7 into 7 advance 1." Remembering the extra 5, we return to place only 2 Earth counters on that upright and raise one Earth counter on the next upright to the left. The board should now indicate 6672.

194

A B C D

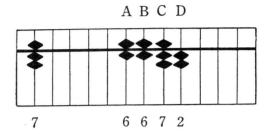

. 7   6 6 7 2

(3) Dividing the 6 on the B upright of the dividend by the divisor, we get, "7 into 6, 8 and 4 over." Instead of returning to place the counters which indicate 6 on B upright, add two Earth counters to them and raise four Earth counters on the next upright to the right. But this next step is impossible, as 7 is already indicated on that upright, therefore, we carry the 4 in our minds. The board indicates 6872 but with what we are carrying in our minds, indicates 68 (11) 2.

4 (carried in mind)

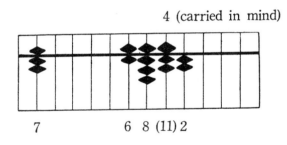

7   6 8 (11) 2

(4) As we could not add the four Earth counters to the 7, we must subtract 3 from the 7 indicated on the upright for tens in the dividend, and then raise one Earth counter on the next upright to the left, as to divide by 7, we, "7, into 7 advance 1." The board should now indicate 6942.

195

A B C D

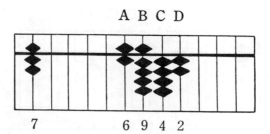

7   6 9 4 2

(5) Dividing the 4 on the C upright by the divisor, we get, "7 into 4, 5 and 5 over." Slide down the Heaven counter on the C upright, and at the same time return to place the four Earth counters on the same upright. Then slide down the Heaven counter on the next upright to the right. The board should now indicate 6957.

A B C D

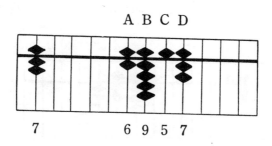

7   6 9 5 7

(6) Dividing the 7 on the D upright by the divisor, we get, "7 into 7 advance 1." Return to place the counters which indicate 7 on the D upright and raise one Earth counter on the next upright to the left, or the C upright.

696 is indicated on the board. It is the quotient.

Part 3.

Division Table by Transfiguration.

When the first figure of the divisor is the same as the first figure of the dividend and the second figure of the divisor is larger than the second figure of the dividend, there is another method of division used. This is called Division by Transfiguration, that is a change of figures.

I will show you this method by examples.

$$\text{Divisor} \quad 15) \overline{135} \quad \begin{array}{l} 9 \quad \text{quotient} \\ \text{dividend} \end{array}$$

A B C D

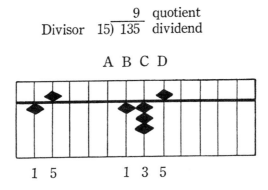

1 5   1 3 5

(1) Dividing the 1 on the first upright of the dividend by the 1 on the first upright of the divisor, we get, "1 into 1 advance 1." Return to place the Earth counter on the first upright of the dividend and raise one Earth counter on the next upright to the left.

1035 should be indicated on the board.

197

A B C D

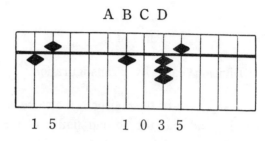

1 5   1 0 3 5

(2) If we multiply the 1 of the temporary quotient on the A upright by the 5 on the end upright of the divisor, we get, "1 × 5 is 5." But we cannot subtract this 5 from the 3 on the upright for tens in the dividend, and having no other resource, we must take back the Earth counter which we advanced to the A upright. In such cases as this we must use the Division Table by Transfiguration.

"looking at the 1, indicate 91 without dividing."

(3) Return to place the Earth counter on the A upright of the dividend and indicate 9 on the next upright to the right, or the upright for 100's in the dividend, and raise one Earth counter on the next upright to the right, or the upright for 10's in the dividend. 945 should be indicated on the board.

A B C D

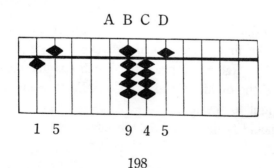

1 5   9 4 5

(4) Multiplying the 9 of the temporary quotient on the first upright of the dividend by the 5 on the last upright of the divisor, we get, "9×5 are 45." Return to place the four Earth counters on the upright for 10's in the dividend and the Heaven counter on the last upright.

9 is indicated on the board. It is the quotient.

As we mentioned above, there is a Division Table to be used when we cannot use the ordinary Division Table. It is as follows :

Rule for 1. Looking at the 1, indicate 91
              without dividing

Rule for 2, Looking at the 2, indicate 92
              without dividing

Rule for 3, Looking at the 3, indicate 93
              without dividing

Rule for 4, Looking at the 4, indicate 94
              without dividing

Rule for 5, Looking at the 5, indicate 95
              without dividing

Rule for 6. Looking at the 6, indicate 96
              without dividing

Rule for 7. Looking at the 7, indicate 97
              without dividing

Part 4.

Practical use of the Division Table by Transfiguration.

Example 1.

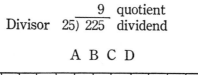

Divisor 25) 225 dividend
              9   quotient

A B C D

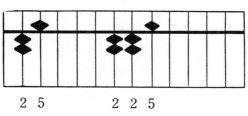

2 5   2 2 5

As the 2 on the first upright of the divisor is the same as
the first figure of the dividend, and the 5 on the second
upright of the divisor is larger than the 2 on the second
upright of the dividend, we must use the rule for 2.

(1) Dividing the 2 on the first upright of the dividend by
the 2 on the first upright of the divisor, we get, "2 into 2

200

advance 1." Return to place the two Earth counters on the first upright of the dividend and raise one Earth counter on the next upright to the left, or the A upright. The board should now indicate 1025.

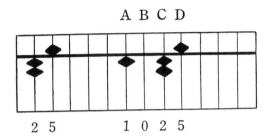

A B C D

2 5   1 0 2 5

(2). If we multiply the 5 on the last upright of the divisor by the 1 of the temporary quotient on the A upright of the dividend, we get, "1×5 is 5," but we cannot subtract this 5 from the 2 on the C upright of the dividend, so we must take back the 2 which was advanced to the A upright, and using the Division Table for 2, we get, "looking at the 2, indicate 92 without dividing." We now change the 2 on the B upright to 9, and add two Earth counters on the next upright to the right, or the C upright. The board should now indicate 945.

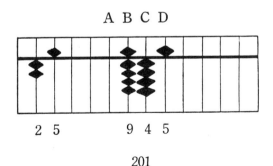

A B C D

2 5   9 4 5

201

Multiplying the 9 of the temporary quotient on the B upright of the dividend and the 5 on the last upright of the divisor, we get, "5×9 are 45." Return to place the four Earth counters on the C upright and the Heaven counter on the D upright.

9 is indicated on the board. It is the quotient.

Example 2.

$$\begin{array}{r} 9 \\ 47{\overline{\smash{)}\,423}} \end{array} \text{ quotient}$$

Divisor 47) 423 dividend

A B C D

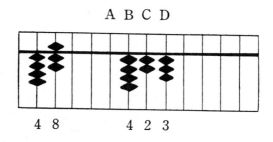

4 8   4 2 3

As the 4 on the first upright of the divisor is the same as the 4 on the first upright of the dividend, and the 7 on the second upright of the divisor is larger than the 2 on the second upright of the dividend, we must use the rule for 4.

(1) Dividing the 4 on the first upright of the dividend by the 4 on the first upright of the divisor, we get, "4 into 4 advance 1." Return to place the four Earth counters on the

first upright of the dividend and raise one Earth counter on the next upright to the left, or the A upright. 1023 should be indicated on the board.

A B C D

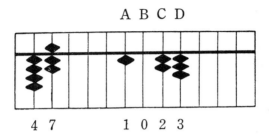

4 7   1 0 2 3

(2) If we multiply the 1 of the temporary quotient on the A upright of the dividend by the 7 on the last upright of the divisor, we get, "1×7 is 7", but we cannot subtract the 7 from the 2 on the C upright of the dividend, therefore, we must take back the 4 counters which were advanced to the A upright and using the rule for 4, we get, "looking at the 4, indicate 94 without dividing." Changing the 4 to 9 and adding four Earth counters on the next upright to the right, we should get 963 indicated on the board.

A B C D

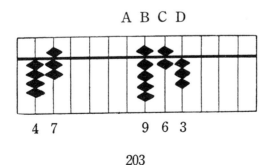

4 7   9 6 3

(3) Multiplying the 9 of the temporary quotient on the first upright of the dividend and the 7 on the last upright of the divisor, we get, "7×9 are 63." Return to place the counters which indicate 6 on the C upright and the three Earth counters on the D upright.

9 is indicated on the board. It is the quotient.

In the following exercises, find the quotient. Cover the answers with a card. If your work is correct, there will be no remainders.

$$25 \overline{)\,2425} \qquad 34 \overline{)\,3128} \qquad 86 \overline{)\,8428}$$

Use rule for 2   Use rule for 3   Use rule for 8

Answer 97   Answer 92   Answer 98

Part 5.

Division Table by Replacement.

This division table is used in the following ways. After having divided the first figure of the dividend by the first figure of the divisor, and multiplying the first figure of the temporary quotient by the second figure of the divisor, we find that we cannot subtract the product from the figure on the lower upright of the dividend, so we must borrow 1 or 2 and place it on the next upright to the right. Then we multiply again, using the figure which was left after subtracting, and the product can now be subtracted from the figure on the lower upright of the dividend. In such cases we use the Division Table by Replacement. I will show you by example.

$$\frac{3}{15) \overline{45}} \quad \substack{\text{quotient} \\ \text{dividend}}$$

Divisor

A B C

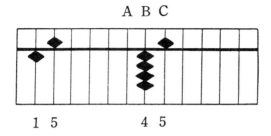

1 5   4 5

(1)   Dividing the 4 on the first upright of the dividend by the 1 on the first upright of the divisor, we get, "1 into 4 advance 4." Return to place the four Earth counters on the first upright of the dividend and raise four Earth counters on the next upright to the left, or the A upright. The board should indicate 105.

A B C

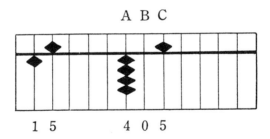

1 5   4 0 5

(2)   Multiplying the 4 of the temporary quotient on the first upright of the dividend by the 5 on the last upright of the divisor, we get, "4×5 are 20", but we cannot subtract the 20 from the 5 on the C upright of the dividend, so we must use the Division Table by Replacement.

(3)   We take one Earth counter from the 4 on the A upright of the temporary quotient and place it on the B upright. 315 will then be indicated on the board.

A B C

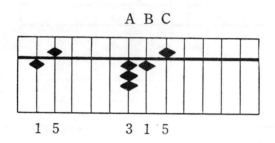

1 5   3 1 5

(4)   Multiplying the 3 on the A upright of the temporary quotient by the 5 on the last upright of the divisor, we get, "3×5 are 15." Now, return to place the Earth counter on the B upright of the dividend and the Heaven counter on the C upright.

3 is indicated on the board. It is the quotient.

In such cases we use the Division Table by Replacement, which is as follows:

Rule for 1 (When we have 1 on the first upright of
                   the divisor)
"Subtract 1, place 1 on the next right hand upright."
Rule for 2 (When we have 2 on the first upright of
                   the divisor)

"Subtract 1, place 2 on the next right hand upright."

Rule for 3 (When we have 3 on the first upright of the divisor)

"Subtract 1, place 3 on the next right hand upright."

Rule for 4 (When we have 4 on the first upright of the divisor)

"Subtract 1, place 4 on the next right hand upright."

Rule for 5 (When we have 5 on the first upright of the divisor)

"Subtract 1, place 5 on the next right hand upright."

Rule for 6 (When we have 6 on the first upright of the divisor)

"Subtract 1, place 6 on the next right hand upright."

Rule for 7 (When we have 7 on the first upright of the divisor)

"Subtract 1, place 7 on the next right hand upright."

Rule for 8 (When we have 8 on the first upright of the divisor)

"Subtract 1, place 8 on the next right hand upright."

Rule for 9 (When we have 9 on the first upright of the divisor)

"Subtract 1, place 9 on the next right hand upright."

Part 6.

Practical use of the Division Table by Replacement.

Example 1.

$$\begin{array}{r} 4 \\ \text{Divisor} \quad 25) \overline{100} \end{array} \quad \begin{array}{l} \text{quotient} \\ \text{dividend} \end{array}$$

A B C

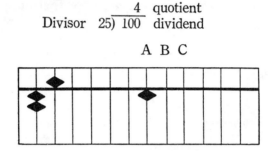

2 5   1 0 0

As we have 2 on the first upright of the divisor, we must use the rule for 2.

(1) Dividing the 1 on the first upright of the dividend by the 2 on the first upright of the divisor, we get, "2 into 1 Heaven 5." Slide down the Heaven counter on the first upright of the dividend, and at the same time return to place the Earth counter on the same upright. The board should indicate 500.

A B C

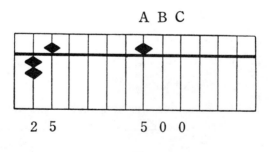

2 5   5 0 0

(2) Multiplying the 5 of the temporary quotient on the first upright of the dividend by the 5 on the last upright of the divisor, we get, "5×5 are 25", but we cannot subtract the 25 from the B and C uprights of the dividend, so we must use the rule for 2, "Subtract 1, place 2 on the next right hand uright." Subtracting 1 from the 5 indicated on the A upright, we get 4, so we return to place the Heaven counter and raise four Earth counters. Next, we raise two Earth counters on the next right hand upright, or the B upright. The board should then indicate 420.

A B C

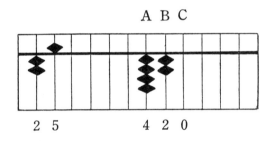

2 5   4 2 0

(3) Multiplying the 4 of the temporary quotient on the first upright of the dividend by the 5 on the last upright of the divisor, we get, "4×5 are 20." Return to place the two Earth counters on the B upright of the dividend.

4 is indicated on the board. It is the quotient.

To sum up the material we have given you, there are three Division Tables :

1. Division Table by Unification.
2. Division Table by Transfiguration.

3. Division Table by Replacement.

These are very important to you, if you wish to master division, for whether you gain speed or not they are very effective.

Section 2.

The Determination of Position.

(1) In cases when the divisor is a whole number:

Beginning with the unit position of the dividend, count off to the left the number of uprights that are contained in the divisor and the next upright to the left is the unit position of the quotient.

A

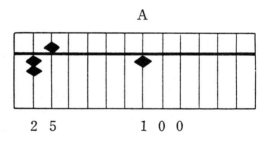

2 5   1 0 0

Divisor   25) $\overline{100}$ dividend

A upright is the unit position of the quotient.

(2) In cases when the divisor is a decimal fraction, such as 0.123:

If we have no zero between the decimal point and the first

210

figure of the fraction, the unit position of the dividend is the unit position of the quotient.

(3) In cases when the divisor is a decimal fraction with zeros to the right of the decimal, such as 0.00123:

Beginning with the unit position of the dividend, count off to the right the number of uprights as there are zeros to the right of the decimal point in the divisor, and the next upright to the right is the unit position for the quotient.

Divisor 0.00123)‾456‾ dividend

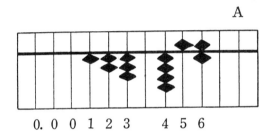

0. 0 0 1 2 3   4 5 6

A upright is the unit position for the quotient.

Section 3.

The Process of Division.

(1) Indicate the dividend on the right hand side of the abacus, and the divisor on the left hand side.

(2) Look at the head figure of the dividend and the head figure of the divisor and get the temporary quotient and

211

determine which of the three Division Tables to use.

(3) Multiply the first figure of the temporary quotient by the second figure of the divisor and subtract the product from the lower uprights of the dividend.

(4) If the divisor contains many uprights, such as 23,456, we must multiply each number by the temporary quotient and subtract the product from the lower uprights of the dividend.

In such cases the unit position of the dividend from which the product is subtracted descends one position with each multiplication. The unit position of the product which we get by multiplying the second figure of the divisor and the first figure of the dividend becomes the position for tens in the next multiplication.

Continuing like this, we descend, one upright at a time, to the last upright of the dividend.

If we subtract the product from every upright of the dividend and still do not have the real quotient, we begin again by dividing the second upright of the dividend by the head upright of the divisor and continue as before.

(5) If we get the whole temporary quotient and we subtract all of the porducts which we get by multiplying every upright of the divisor by the temporary quotient, then we have the real quotient.

(6) If we cannot subtract the product which we get by multiplying the temporary quotient and the second upright of the divisor or any upright beneath it, from the second

upright of the dividend, we must use the Division Table by Replacement.

Part 1.

Practical Training in Division.

Example 1.

$$\begin{array}{r} 12 \text{ quotient} \\ \text{Divisor } 56) \overline{\ 672\ } \text{ dividend} \end{array}$$

A B C D

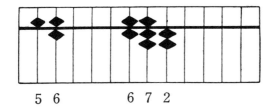

5 6   6 7 2

(1) Indicate the dividend on the right hand side of the board and the divisor on the left hand, as is shown in the above illustration.

(2) Count off the number of uprights which are contained in the divisor to the left, beginning with the unit position of the dividend, and the next left hand upright is the unit position for the quotient, In this case it is the B upright.

(3) Divide the first figure of the dividend by the first figure of the divisor, in this case, "5 into 5 advance 1." Return to place the Heaven counter on the first upright of the

213

dividend and raise one Earth counter on the next upright to the left, or the A upright.   The board should indicate 1172.

A B C D

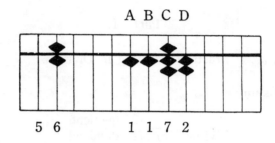

5 6   1 1 7 2

(4) Multiplying the 1 of the temporary quotient on the A upright of the dividend by the 6 on the end upright of the divisor, we get, "1×6 is 6." Subtracting this product from the 7 on the upright for tens in the dividend (In this case the B upright is the position for tens and the C upright is the unit position.), 1112 should be indicated on the board.

A B C D

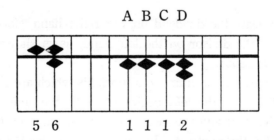

5 6   1 1 1 2

(5) Dividing the 1 on the B upright (not the 1 on the A upright, as it belongs to the temporary quotient) by the 5 on the first upright of the divisor, we get, "5 into 1   plus 1."

Raise one Earth counter on the upright for 100's in the dividend, or the B upright. 1212 should be indicated on the board.

A B C D

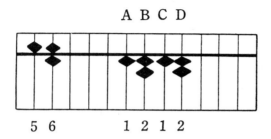

5 6   1 2 1 2

(6) Multiplying the 2 of the temporary quotient on the upright for 100's in the dividend by the 6 on the end upright of the divisor, we get, "2×6 are 12." Return to place the one Earth counter on the upright for 10's, or the C upright and the two Earth counters on the last upright of the dividend.

12 is indicated on the board. It is the quotient.

Example 2.

$$\text{Divisor } 162\overline{)3\stackrel{201}{2}680} \quad \begin{array}{l}\text{quotient, 118 remainder}\\ \text{dividend}\end{array}$$

A B C D E F

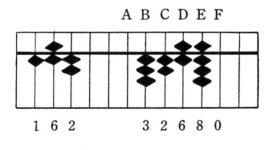

1 6 2   3 2 6 8 0

215

(1) Indicate the divisor on the left hand side of the board, and the dividend to the right of it, as is shown in the above illustration.

(2) Beginning with the unit position of the dividend, count off to the left the number of uprights which are contained in the divisor, and the next left upright is the unit position for the quotient.

(3) Dividing the 3 on the first upright of the dividend by the 1 on the first upright of the divisor, we get, "1 into 3 advance 3." Return to place the 3 Earth counters on the first upright of the dividend and at the same time raise three Earth counters on the next upright to the left, or the A upright. The board should indicate 302680.

A B C D E F

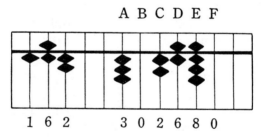

1 6 2   3 0 2 6 8 0

(4) Multiplying the 3 of the temporary quotient on the A upright by the 6 on the second upright of the divisor, we get, "3×6 are 18." But we cannot subtract the 18 from the 2 on the upright for 100's in the dividend.

(5) In this case, therefore, we must use the Division Table, "1 into 2 advance 2." Return to place the two Earth counters on the first upright of the dividend and at the same

216

time raise two Earth counters on the next upright to the left, or the A upright. The board should indicate 212680.

A B C D E F

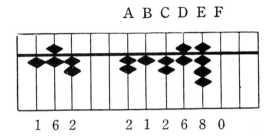

1 6 2   2 1 2 6 8 0

(6) Multiplying the 2 of the temporary quotient on the A upright by the 6 on the upright for 10's in the divisor, we get, "2×6 are 12." Return to place the one Earth counter on the upright for 10000's in the dividend and the two Earth counters on the upright for 1000's. The board should indicate 200680.

A B C D E F

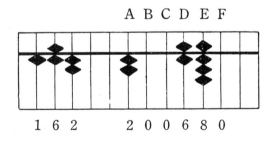

1 6 2   2 0 0 6 8 0

(7) Multiplying the 2 of the temporary quotient on the A upright by the 2 on the last upright of the divisor, we get, "2×2 are 4." Subtract 4 from the 6 indicated on the

upright for 100's of the dividend. The board should now indicate 200280.

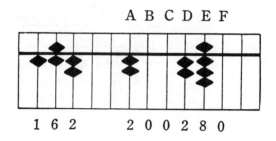

A B C D E F

1 6 2   2 0 0 2 8 0

(8) Dividing the 2 on the upright for 100's in the dividend by the 1 on the first upright of the divisor, we get, " 1 into 2 advance 2." But if we return to place the two Earth counters on the upright for 100's of the dividend and raise two Earth counters on the next upright to the left, we will not be able to subtract the product 12, which we get by multiplying the 2 of the temporary quotient on the upright for 1000's in the dividend by the 6 on the upright for 10's in the divisor, from the amount indicated on the upright for 100's and for 10's in the dividend.

Therefore, we must use the Division Table, " 1 into 1 advance 1 ", and return to place one of the Earth counters on the upright for 100's in the dividend and raise one Earth counter on the next upright to the left, or the C upright. The board should indicate 201180.

218

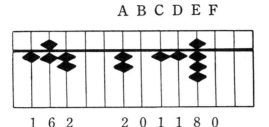

A B C D E F

1 6 2   2 0 1 1 8 0

(9) Multiplying the 1 of the second temporary quotient on the upright for 1000's in the dividend by the 6 on the upright for 10's in the divisor, we get, "1×6 is 6," Return to place the counters which indicate 6 from the 8 on the upright for 10's in the dividend. The board should indidate 201120.

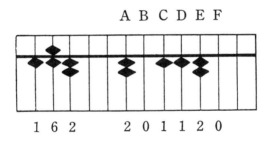

A B C D E F

1 6 2   2 0 1 1 2 0

(10) Multiplying the 1 of the second temporary quotient on the upright for 1000's in the dividend by the 2 on the last upright of the divisor, we get, "1×2 is 2." We want to subtract this two from the last upright of the dividend, but as there is a zero there, we must think, "2 from 10 is 8." Then we return to place one Earth counter on the upright for 10's of the dividend and at the same time indicate 8 on the next upright to the right, or the last upright of the dividend. The board should now indicate 201118.

219

The C upright was the upright which we found to be the
unit position of the quotient at the beginning of our division.
Therefore, the 201 indicated on the A, B, and C uprights is
the quotient, and the 118 on the D, E and F uprights is the
remainder.

quotient   201
remainder   118

Part   2.

Find the quotients and the remainders in the following
problems. If there is no remainder, write after the quotient,
"and no remainder."

Check your answers by multiplying the quotient by the
divisor and adding the remainder.

(1)	(2)	(3)
21) 466	36) 1278	25) 425

(4)	(5)	(6)
69) 2208	27) 513	23) 322

Find the quotients and check answers.

(1)	(2)	(3)
42) $ 63.84	52) $ 110.76	14) $ 71.12

(4)	(5)	(6)
16) $ 15.68	34) $ 38.08	27) $ 146.34

Practice examples for Division.

Find the quotient and the remainder.

(1) divisor   25)‾432‾   dividend

(2) divisor   108)‾1404‾   dividend

(3) divisor   98)‾2548‾   dividend

(4) divisor   27)‾244‾   dividend

(5) divisor   16)‾4032‾   dividend

(6) divisor   12)‾1668‾   dividend

(7) divisor   14)‾567‾   dividend

(8) divisor   54)‾1026‾   dividend

(9) divisor   36)‾972‾   dividend

(10) divisor   45)‾525‾   dividend

Key to the above problems.

   (1)   17 and 7 over

   (2)   13

   (3)   26

   (4)   9 and 1 over

   (5)   252

   (6)   139

   (7)   40 and 7 over

   (8)   19

   (9)   27

   (10)   11 and 30 over

CHAPTER VII.

DIVISION BY ABBREVIATION

This method of division uses the Multiplication Tables only and is like division in writing.

Section 1.

The Determination of Position.

(1) When the divisor is a whole number, count the number of uprights.

(2) Beginning with the unit position of the dividend, count off towards the left as many uprights as there are in the divisor, and the second next upright to the left is the unit position for the quotient. This is shown in the following illustration.

A B C D

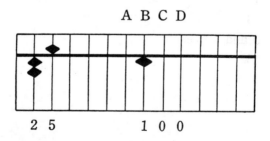

2 5   1 0 0

A upright is the unit position of the quotient.

If we compare the determination of the unit position for the quotient in Division by Abbreviation and Division by Unification, we will see that Division by Abbreviation we must count off one more upright to the left, than in Division by Unification.

Divisor 12)‾345‾ dividend

(a) Division by Unification.

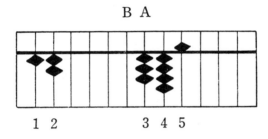

(b) Division by Abbreviation.

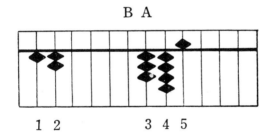

(a) A upright is the unit position.
(b) B upright is the unit position.

(3) In cases when the divisor is a decimal fraction such as 0.123 and there is no zero between the decimal point and the first figure, the next upright to the left of the unit position of the dividend is the unit position for the quotient.

(4) In cases when the divisor is a decimal fraction such as 0.00123, count the number of uprights which contain zero between the decimal point and the first figure and subtract 1 from this number, then count off this many uprights toward the right beginning with the unit position of the dividend and the next upright to the right is the unit position for the quotient.

Section 2.

The Process of Division by Abbreviation.

Type 1.

(1) Indicate the divisor on the left hand side of the abacus and the dividend to the right of it.

(2) We must divide the dividend into groups containing the same number of uprights as there are in the divisor. If we have a two place number for the divisor, we must divide the entire dividend into groups of two as is shown in the following illustration.

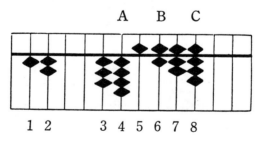

A   B   C

1 2   3 4 5 6 7 8

(3) Taking the first group only, we think of how many times the divisor is contained into this group.

(4) When we get the first temporary quotient in this way, we indicate it on the second upright to the left from the first upright of the dividend.

(5) Then we multiply the temporary quotient by the first upright of the divisor and subtract the product from the first number.

(6) In this way we must multiply every upright of the divisor by the first temporary quotient, and if we are able to subtract the product within the boundary of the first group, then we see how many times the divisor is contained in the second group.

(7) After we thus get the second temporary quotient, we indicate it on the next upright to the right of the first temporary quotient.

(8) Then we multiply the second temporary quotient by the first upright of the divisor and when we get the product, subtract it from the second group of the dividend.

(9) When we have proceeded in this way with every group of the dividend, we will have the real quotient and the remainder.

Section 3.

The Process of Division by Abbreviation.

Type 2.

(1) Indicate the divisor on the left hand side of the board and the dividend to the right of it.

(2)   After we have divided the dividend into groups which have the same number of uprights as the divisor, we sometimes find that we cannot subtract some of the products from the number within the group, as is shown in the following:

$$\text{Divisor} \quad 20)\overline{21123} \quad \text{dividend}$$

As 20 is a two-place number, we divide the dividend into three groups, as follows: 21, 12, 3. But 20 will not go into the 12 of the second group, therefore, we must add one more upright and divide the dividend in the following way: 21, 123.

(3)   In such a case we must be careful in placing the temporary quotient. It should be indicated on the next upright to the right of where it would ordinarily be placed.

When you multiply the temporary quotient by some upright of the divisor and get a number too large to subtract from the number in the group with which you are dealing, you proceed in just the same manner as you do when the number cannot be divided by the divisor.

(4)   When the temporary quotient has three places or more, it is difficult to figure in our minds how many times the divisor of two places is contained in it. It will help us to consider the first figure of the dividend and see how many times the first figure of the divisor will go into it. For example, when you are dividing 72 by 21, think how many times 2 goes into 7.

226

Section 4.

Practical Training in Division by Abbreviation

Example 1.

$$\begin{array}{r} 24 \text{ quotient} \\ \text{Divisor } 3\overline{)\ 72} \text{ dividend} \end{array}$$

A

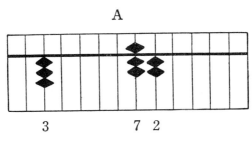

3   7 2

(1) Indicate the divisor on the left of the abacus and the dividend to the right of it, as is shown in the above illustration.

(2) Beginning with the unit position of the dividend, count off to the left the number of uprights which are contained in the divisor and the second upright to the left of that one is the unit position for the quotient.

(3) As the divisor is a one-place number, we must divide the dividend into groups containing one upright.

(4) By looking at the board we see that we must divide the 7 on the first upright of the dividend by the divisor which is 3.

(5) As 3 goes into 7 two times, we must raise two Earth counters on the second upright to the left of the first upright of the dividend. The board should indicate 2072.

A

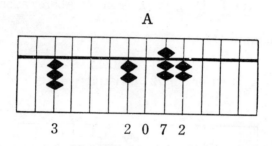

3   2 0 7 2

(6) Multiplying the 2 of the temporary quotient by the 3 of the divisor, we get, "2×3 are 6." Return to place 6 of the 7 indicated on the upright for 10's in the dividend. The board should now indicate 2012.

A

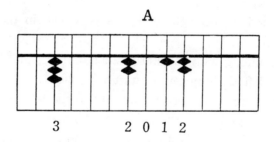

3   2 0 1 2

(7) As the divisor 3 will not go into the 1 on the upright for 10's in the dividend, we must add one more upright to it, then 3 will go into 12, 4 times.

(8) We must indicate this 4 on the next upright to the

228

right of the first temporary quotient. The board should indicate 2412.

A

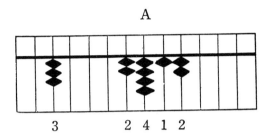

3   2 4 1 2

(9) Multiplying the 4 of the second temporary quotient by the divisor, we get, "3×4 are 12." Return to place the Earth counter on the upright for 10's in the dividend and the two Earth counters on the last upright.

24 is indicated on the board. It is the quotient.

Example 2.

$$\begin{array}{r} 14 \text{ quotient} \\ \text{Divisor } 26) \overline{364} \text{ dividend} \end{array}$$

A B C D E

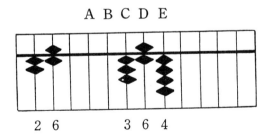

2 6   3 6 4

(1) Place the divisor on the left hand side of the board,

229

and the dividend to the right of it, as is shown in the above illustration.

(2) Beginning with the unit position of the diviend, count off towards the left the number of uprights which are contained in the divisor, and the second upright to the left of that will be the unit position for the quotient.

(3) As the divisor is a two-place number, divide the dividend into groups of two places.

(4) As the first group is 36, we can see that the divisor goes into this only once.

(5) Raise one Earth counter on the second upright to the left of the first upright of the dividend. The board should indicate 10364.

A B C D E

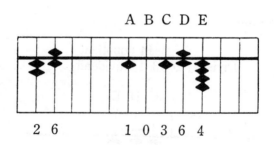

2 6   1 0 3 6 4

(6) Multiplying the 1 of the temporary quotient by the 2, which is the first figure of the divisor, we get, "1×2 is 2." Return to place two Earth counters on the upright for 100's in the dividend. The board should indicate 10164.

A B C D E

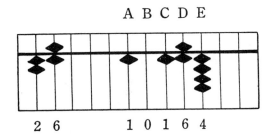

2 6   1 0 1 6 4

(7) Multiplying the temporary quotient by the second figure of the divisor, we get, "1×6 is 6." Return to place the counters which indicate 6 on the second upright of the first group of the dividend. The board should indicate 10104.

A B C D E

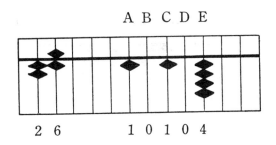

2 6   1 0 1 0 4

(8) As 26 will not go into 10, we must add one more upright and we find that 26 will go into 104 four times.

(9) We must indicate this 4 on the next upright to the right of the first temporary quotient. The board should now indicate 14104.

A B C D E

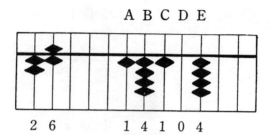

2 6   1 4 1 0 4

(10) Multiplying the 4 of the second temporary quotient on the upright for 1000's in the dividend by the 2, which is the first figure of the divisor, we get, "2×4 are 8." Return to place 8 of the 10 of the second group. The board should indicate 14024.

A B C D E

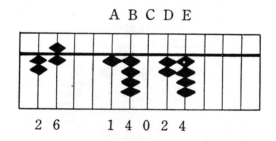

2 6   1 4 0 2 4

(11) Multiplying the 4 of the second temporary quotient by the 6 which is the second figure of the divisor, we get, "4×6 are 24." Return to place the two Earth counters on the upright for 10's in the dividend and the 4 Earth counters on the last upright.

14 is indicated on the board. It is the quotient.

In the beginning of this example, we found that the unit

position of the quotient was on the upright for 1,000's in the dividend, or the B upright. Therefore, 14 is the real quotient.

By now, I think that division should be plain to you. I hope that you will be diligent in practicing and reviewing, so that you can compute any number easily.

I am glad that by now you can add, subtract, multiply, and divide on the abacus.

Do not be afraid of even the largest numbers, as the process is just the same as you have learned.

Turn to page 193 and compare it with this page.

$$\begin{array}{r} 696 \text{quotient} \\ \text{Divisor} \quad 7)\overline{4872} \quad \text{dividend} \end{array}$$

A B C D E

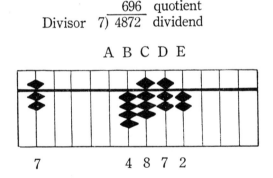

7   4 8 7 2

(1) As the divisor is a one upright number, divide the dividend into groups containing one upright each.

(2) As 7 will not go into 4, we must take one more upright into the first group. Then 7 will go into 48 six times.

(3) Place this 6 on the next upright to the left of the first upright of the dividend, or one upright to the right of where it should have gone if we had not borrowed one number from the second group. The board should indicate 64872.

A B C D E

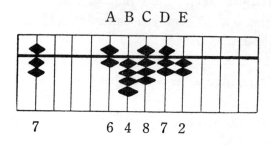

7   6 4 8 7 2

(4) Multiplying the 6 of the first temporary quotient by the divisor, we get, "6×7 are 42." Subtract the 4 from the upright for 1000's in the dividend and the 2 from the upright for 100's in the dividend. The board should indicate 60672.

A B C D E

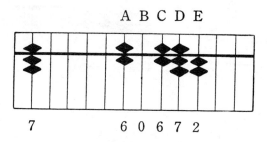

7   6 0 6 7 2

(5) The divisor will not go into the next group, which is 6, therefore, we must borrow one upright. 7 goes into 67 nine times.

234

(6) Place this product 9 on the next upright to the right of the first temporary quotient, in this case the B upright. The board should indicate 69672.

A B C D E

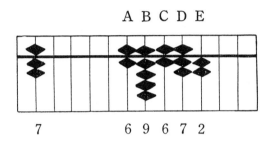

7   6 9 6 7 2

(7) Multiplying the 9 of the second temporary quotient on the upright for 1000's in the dividend by the divisor, we get, "7×9 are 63." Subtract 6 from the upright for 100's in the dividend and 3 from the upright for 10's. The board should indicate 69042.

A B C D E

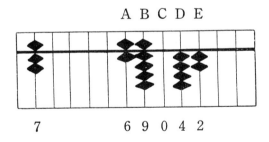

7   6 9 0 4 2

(8) The divisor will not go into the next group, so we must again borrow one upright. Then 7 will go into 42 six times.

(9) Place this 6 on the next upright to the right from the second temporary quotient, in this case the C upright. The board should indicate 69642.

A B C D E

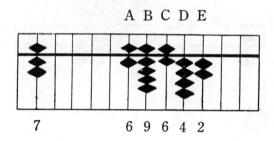

7   6 9 6 4 2

(10) Multiplying the 6 of the third temporary quotient on the upright for 100's in the dividend by the divisor, we get, "6×7 are 42." Subtract the 4 from the upright for 10's in the dividend and the 2 from the last upright.

696 is indicated on the board. It is the quotient.

In the beginning of the division we found that the unit position of the quotient was the C upright. Therefore, 696 is the real quotient,

Find the quotient.

Row A

(1) 36) 23364

(2) 43) 31089

Row A

(1) 64) 16512

(2) 68) 26316

236

(3) 48)$\overline{42960}$ (3) 72)$\overline{30600}$

(4) 55)$\overline{50270}$ (4) 76)$\overline{39368}$

(5) 59)$\overline{9558}$ (5) 85)$\overline{54315}$

(6) 7)$\overline{4872}$ (6) 24)$\overline{75288}$

(7) 8)$\overline{6232}$ (7) 35)$\overline{186305}$

(8) 9)$\overline{7758}$ (8) 41)$\overline{288558}$

(9) 2)$\overline{1886}$ (9) 19)$\overline{42921}$

(10) 3)$\overline{468}$ (10) 87)$\overline{64467}$

For the Salesman.

The abacus is very convenient for the salesman in computing change.

The price of the goods is $ 1.26
Clerk receives $ 5.00

1 2 6   Employed counters
3 7 4   Unemployed counters

(1) As shown in the above illustration the clerk should indicate the price of the goods on the board, in this case it is $ 1.26.

(2) Discounting one on every upright except the last one and the Heaven counter on the first upright, the number of unemployed counters will give the clerk the amount of change required.

(3) 3 counters are unemployed on the upright for 100's, counters indicating 7 on the upright for 10's and 4 counters on the upright for 1's; 374 is indicated. This is the same as $ 3.74, which is the amount of change.

238

The price of goods $ 3.82
Clerk receives $ 10.00

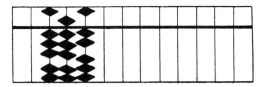

3 8 2 Employed counters
6 1 8 Unemployed counters

(1) As is shown in the above illustration, place the price of the goods on the board. $3.82 is indicated as 382.

(2) Find out how many unemployed counters there are, instead of thinking 382 and so many make 1000.

(3) There are 6 on the upright for 100's and 1 on the upright for 10's and 8 on the end upright.

The amount of the change is $6.18.

If the salesman uses an abacus in computing change, he can be not only quick but accurate. Therefore even if the amount is small you should use an abacus.

(1) $ .28¢ Price of goods
        $ 1.00   Money received
        $ .72¢   Change

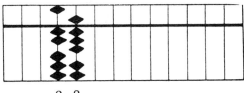

2 8
7 2..............Surplus

(2) $ 2.73 Price of goods
     $ 5.00 Money received
     $ 2.27 Change

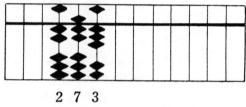

        2 7 3
        2 2 7...............Surplus

(3) $ 6.19 Price of goods
     $ 10.00 Money received
     $ 3.81 Change

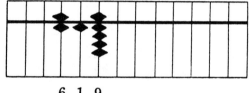

        6 1 9
        3 8 1...............Surplus

Always when you give back change you should add the amount to the price of the goods to check yourself. If the sum equals the money received you have given back the correct amount.

240

A CATALOGUE OF SELECTED DOVER BOOKS
IN ALL FIELDS OF INTEREST

A CATALOGUE OF SELECTED DOVER BOOKS
IN ALL FIELDS OF INTEREST

WHAT IS SCIENCE?, *N. Campbell*
The role of experiment and measurement, the function of mathematics, the nature of scientific laws, the difference between laws and theories, the limitations of science, and many similarly provocative topics are treated clearly and without technicalities by an eminent scientist. "Still an excellent introduction to scientific philosophy," H. Margenau in *Physics Today*. "A first-rate primer . . . deserves a wide audience," *Scientific American*. 192pp. 5⅜ x 8.
Paperbound $1.25

THE NATURE OF LIGHT AND COLOUR IN THE OPEN AIR, *M. Minnaert*
Why are shadows sometimes blue, sometimes green, or other colors depending on the light and surroundings? What causes mirages? Why do multiple suns and moons appear in the sky? Professor Minnaert explains these unusual phenomena and hundreds of others in simple, easy-to-understand terms based on optical laws and the properties of light and color. No mathematics is required but artists, scientists, students, and everyone fascinated by these "tricks" of nature will find thousands of useful and amazing pieces of information. Hundreds of observational experiments are suggested which require no special equipment. 200 illustrations; 42 photos. xvi + 362pp. 5⅜ x 8.
Paperbound $2.00

THE STRANGE STORY OF THE QUANTUM, AN ACCOUNT FOR THE GENERAL READER OF THE GROWTH OF IDEAS UNDERLYING OUR PRESENT ATOMIC KNOWLEDGE, *B. Hoffmann*
Presents lucidly and expertly, with barest amount of mathematics, the problems and theories which led to modern quantum physics. Dr. Hoffmann begins with the closing years of the 19th century, when certain trifling discrepancies were noticed, and with illuminating analogies and examples takes you through the brilliant concepts of Planck, Einstein, Pauli, Broglie, Bohr, Schroedinger, Heisenberg, Dirac, Sommerfeld, Feynman, etc. This edition includes a new, long postscript carrying the story through 1958. "Of the books attempting an account of the history and contents of our modern atomic physics which have come to my attention, this is the best," H. Margenau, Yale University, in *American Journal of Physics*. 32 tables and line illustrations. Index. 275pp. 5⅜ x 8.
Paperbound $1.75

GREAT IDEAS OF MODERN MATHEMATICS: THEIR NATURE AND USE, *Jagjit Singh*
Reader with only high school math will understand main mathematical ideas of modern physics, astronomy, genetics, psychology, evolution, etc. better than many who use them as tools, but comprehend little of their basic structure. Author uses his wide knowledge of non-mathematical fields in brilliant exposition of differential equations, matrices, group theory, logic, statistics, problems of mathematical foundations, imaginary numbers, vectors, etc. Original publication. 2 appendixes. 2 indexes. 65 ills. 322pp. 5⅜ x 8.
Paperbound $2.00

THE MUSIC OF THE SPHERES: THE MATERIAL UNIVERSE — FROM ATOM TO QUASAR, SIMPLY EXPLAINED, *Guy Murchie*
Vast compendium of fact, modern concept and theory, observed and calculated data, historical background guides intelligent layman through the material universe. Brilliant exposition of earth's construction, explanations for moon's craters, atmospheric components of Venus and Mars (with data from recent fly-by's), sun spots, sequences of star birth and death, neighboring galaxies, contributions of Galileo, Tycho Brahe, Kepler, etc.; and (Vol. 2) construction of the atom (describing newly discovered sigma and xi subatomic particles), theories of sound, color and light, space and time, including relativity theory, quantum theory, wave theory, probability theory, work of Newton, Maxwell, Faraday, Einstein, de Broglie, etc. "Best presentation yet offered to the intelligent general reader," *Saturday Review*. Revised (1967). Index. 319 illustrations by the author. Total of xx + 644pp. 5⅜ x 8½.
Vol. 1 Paperbound $2.00, Vol. 2 Paperbound $2.00,
The set $4.00

FOUR LECTURES ON RELATIVITY AND SPACE, *Charles Proteus Steinmetz*
Lecture series, given by great mathematician and electrical engineer, generally considered one of the best popular-level expositions of special and general relativity theories and related questions. Steinmetz translates complex mathematical reasoning into language accessible to laymen through analogy, example and comparison. Among topics covered are relativity of motion, location, time; of mass; acceleration; 4-dimensional time-space; geometry of the gravitational field; curvature and bending of space; non-Euclidean geometry. Index. 40 illustrations. x + 142pp. 5⅜ x 8½. Paperbound $1.35

HOW TO KNOW THE WILD FLOWERS, *Mrs. William Starr Dana*
Classic nature book that has introduced thousands to wonders of American wild flowers. Color-season principle of organization is easy to use, even by those with no botanical training, and the genial, refreshing discussions of history, folklore, uses of over 1,000 native and escape flowers, foliage plants are informative as well as fun to read. Over 170 full-page plates, collected from several editions, may be colored in to make permanent records of finds. Revised to conform with 1950 edition of Gray's Manual of Botany. xlii + 438pp. 5⅜ x 8½. Paperbound $2.00

MANUAL OF THE TREES OF NORTH AMERICA, *Charles Sprague Sargent*
Still unsurpassed as most comprehensive, reliable study of North American tree characteristics, precise locations and distribution. By dean of American dendrologists. Every tree native to U.S., Canada, Alaska; 185 genera, 717 species, described in detail—leaves, flowers, fruit, winterbuds, bark, wood, growth habits, etc. plus discussion of varieties and local variants, immaturity variations. Over 100 keys, including unusual 11-page analytical key to genera, aid in identification. 783 clear illustrations of flowers, fruit, leaves. An unmatched permanent reference work for all nature lovers. Second enlarged (1926) edition. Synopsis of families. Analytical key to genera. Glossary of technical terms. Index. 783 illustrations, 1 map. Total of 982pp. 5⅜ x 8.
Vol. 1 Paperbound $2.25, Vol. 2 Paperbound $2.25,
The set $4.50

IT'S FUN TO MAKE THINGS FROM SCRAP MATERIALS,
Evelyn Glantz Hershoff
What use are empty spools, tin cans, bottle tops? What can be made from rubber bands, clothes pins, paper clips, and buttons? This book provides simply worded instructions and large diagrams showing you how to make cookie cutters, toy trucks, paper turkeys, Halloween masks, telephone sets, aprons, linoleum block- and spatter prints — in all 399 projects! Many are easy enough for young children to figure out for themselves; some challenging enough to entertain adults; all are remarkably ingenious ways to make things from materials that cost pennies or less! Formerly "Scrap Fun for Everyone." Index. 214 illustrations. 373pp. 5⅜ x 8½.   Paperbound $1.50

SYMBOLIC LOGIC and THE GAME OF LOGIC, *Lewis Carroll*
"Symbolic Logic" is not concerned with modern symbolic logic, but is instead a collection of over 380 problems posed with charm and imagination, using the syllogism and a fascinating diagrammatic method of drawing conclusions. In "The Game of Logic" Carroll's whimsical imagination devises a logical game played with 2 diagrams and counters (included) to manipulate hundreds of tricky syllogisms. The final section, "Hit or Miss" is a lagniappe of 101 additional puzzles in the delightful Carroll manner. Until this reprint edition, both of these books were rarities costing up to $15 each. Symbolic Logic: Index. xxxi + 199pp. The Game of Logic: 96pp. 2 vols. bound as one. 5⅜ x 8.
Paperbound $2.00

MATHEMATICAL PUZZLES OF SAM LOYD, PART I
selected and edited by M. Gardner
Choice puzzles by the greatest American puzzle creator and innovator. Selected from his famous collection, "Cyclopedia of Puzzles," they retain the unique style and historical flavor of the originals. There are posers based on arithmetic, algebra, probability, game theory, route tracing, topology, counter and sliding block, operations research, geometrical dissection. Includes the famous "14-15" puzzle which was a national craze, and his "Horse of a Different Color" which sold millions of copies. 117 of his most ingenious puzzles in all. 120 line drawings and diagrams. Solutions. Selected references. xx + 167pp. 5⅜ x 8.
Paperbound $1.00

STRING FIGURES AND HOW TO MAKE THEM, *Caroline Furness Jayne*
107 string figures plus variations selected from the best primitive and modern examples developed by Navajo, Apache, pygmies of Africa, Eskimo, in Europe, Australia, China, etc. The most readily understandable, easy-to-follow book in English on perennially popular recreation. Crystal-clear exposition; step-by-step diagrams. Everyone from kindergarten children to adults looking for unusual diversion will be endlessly amused. Index. Bibliography. Introduction by A. C. Haddon. 17 full-page plates, 960 illustrations. xxiii + 401pp. 5⅜ x 8½.
Paperbound $2.00

PAPER FOLDING FOR BEGINNERS, *W. D. Murray and F. J. Rigney*
A delightful introduction to the varied and entertaining Japanese art of origami (paper folding), with a full, crystal-clear text that anticipates every difficulty; over 275 clearly labeled diagrams of all important stages in creation. You get results at each stage, since complex figures are logically developed from simpler ones. 43 different pieces are explained: sailboats, frogs, roosters, etc. 6 photographic plates. 279 diagrams. 95pp. 5⅜ x 8⅜. Paperbound $1.00

PRINCIPLES OF ART HISTORY,
H. Wölfflin
Analyzing such terms as "baroque," "classic," "neoclassic," "primitive," "picturesque," and 164 different works by artists like Botticelli, van Cleve, Dürer, Hobbema, Holbein, Hals, Rembrandt, Titian, Brueghel, Vermeer, and many others, the author establishes the classifications of art history and style on a firm, concrete basis. This classic of art criticism shows what really occurred between the 14th-century primitives and the sophistication of the 18th century in terms of basic attitudes and philosophies. "A remarkable lesson in the art of seeing," *Sat. Rev. of Literature.* Translated from the 7th German edition. 150 illustrations. 254pp. 6⅛ x 9¼. Paperbound $2.00

PRIMITIVE ART,
Franz Boas
This authoritative and exhaustive work by a great American anthropologist covers the entire gamut of primitive art. Pottery, leatherwork, metal work, stone work, wood, basketry, are treated in detail. Theories of primitive art, historical depth in art history, technical virtuosity, unconscious levels of patterning, symbolism, styles, literature, music, dance, etc. A must book for the interested layman, the anthropologist, artist, handicrafter (hundreds of unusual motifs), and the historian. Over 900 illustrations (50 ceramic vessels, 12 totem poles, etc.). 376pp. 5⅜ x 8. Paperbound $2.25

THE GENTLEMAN AND CABINET MAKER'S DIRECTOR,
Thomas Chippendale
A reprint of the 1762 catalogue of furniture designs that went on to influence generations of English and Colonial and Early Republic American furniture makers. The 200 plates, most of them full-page sized, show Chippendale's designs for French (Louis XV), Gothic, and Chinese-manner chairs, sofas, canopy and dome beds, cornices, chamber organs, cabinets, shaving tables, commodes, picture frames, frets, candle stands, chimney pieces, decorations, etc. The drawings are all elegant and highly detailed; many include construction diagrams and elevations. A supplement of 24 photographs shows surviving pieces of original and Chippendale-style pieces of furniture. Brief biography of Chippendale by N. I. Bienenstock, editor of *Furniture World.* Reproduced from the 1762 edition. 200 plates, plus 19 photographic plates. vi + 249pp. 9⅛ x 12¼. Paperbound $3.50

AMERICAN ANTIQUE FURNITURE: A BOOK FOR AMATEURS,
Edgar G. Miller, Jr.
Standard introduction and practical guide to identification of valuable American antique furniture. 2115 illustrations, mostly photographs taken by the author in 148 private homes, are arranged in chronological order in extensive chapters on chairs, sofas, chests, desks, bedsteads, mirrors, tables, clocks, and other articles. Focus is on furniture accessible to the collector, including simpler pieces and a larger than usual coverage of Empire style. Introductory chapters identify structural elements, characteristics of various styles, how to avoid fakes, etc. "We are frequently asked to name some book on American furniture that will meet the requirements of the novice collector, the beginning dealer, and . . . the general public. . . . We believe Mr. Miller's two volumes more completely satisfy this specification than any other work," *Antiques.* Appendix. Index. Total of vi + 1106pp. 7⅞ x 10¾.
Two volume set, paperbound $7.50

THE BAD CHILD'S BOOK OF BEASTS, MORE BEASTS FOR WORSE CHILDREN, and A MORAL ALPHABET, *H. Belloc*
Hardly and anthology of humorous verse has appeared in the last 50 years without at least a couple of these famous nonsense verses: But one must see the entire volumes — with all the delightful original illustrations by Sir Basil Blackwood — to appreciate fully Belloc's charming and witty verses that play so subacidly on the platitudes of life and morals that beset his day — and ours. A great humor classic. Three books in one. Total of 157pp. 5⅜ x 8.
Paperbound $1.00

THE DEVIL'S DICTIONARY, *Ambrose Bierce*
Sardonic and irreverent barbs puncturing the pomposities and absurdities of American politics, business, religion, literature, and arts, by the country's greatest satirist in the classic tradition. Epigrammatic as Shaw, piercing as Swift, American as Mark Twain, Will Rogers, and Fred Allen, Bierce will always remain the favorite of a small coterie of enthusiasts, and of writers and speakers whom he supplies with "some of the most gorgeous witticisms of the English language" (H. L. Mencken). Over 1000 entries in alphabetical order. 144pp. 5⅜ x 8.
Paperbound $1.00

THE COMPLETE NONSENSE OF EDWARD LEAR.
This is the only complete edition of this master of gentle madness available at a popular price. *A Book of Nonsense, Nonsense Songs, More Nonsense Songs and Stories* in their entirety with all the old favorites that have delighted children and adults for years. The Dong With A Luminous Nose, The Jumblies, The Owl and the Pussycat, and hundreds of other bits of wonderful nonsense. 214 limericks, 3 sets of Nonsense Botany, 5 Nonsense Alphabets, 546 drawings by Lear himself, and much more. 320pp. 5⅜ x 8.
Paperbound $1.00

THE WIT AND HUMOR OF OSCAR WILDE, *ed. by Alvin Redman*
Wilde at his most brilliant, in 1000 epigrams exposing weaknesses and hypocrisies of "civilized" society. Divided into 49 categories—sin, wealth, women, America, etc.—to aid writers, speakers. Includes excerpts from his trials, books, plays, criticism. Formerly "The Epigrams of Oscar Wilde." Introduction by Vyvyan Holland, Wilde's only living son. Introductory essay by editor. 260pp. 5⅜ x 8.
Paperbound $1.00

A CHILD'S PRIMER OF NATURAL HISTORY, *Oliver Herford*
Scarcely an anthology of whimsy and humor has appeared in the last 50 years without a contribution from Oliver Herford. Yet the works from which these examples are drawn have been almost impossible to obtain! Here at last are Herford's improbable definitions of a menagerie of familiar and weird animals, each verse illustrated by the author's own drawings. 24 drawings in 2 colors; 24 additional drawings. vii + 95pp. 6½ x 6.
Paperbound $1.00

THE BROWNIES: THEIR BOOK, *Palmer Cox*
The book that made the Brownies a household word. Generations of readers have enjoyed the antics, predicaments and adventures of these jovial sprites, who emerge from the forest at night to play or to come to the aid of a deserving human. Delightful illustrations by the author decorate nearly every page. 24 short verse tales with 266 illustrations. 155pp. 6⅝ x 9¼.
Paperbound $1.50

THE PRINCIPLES OF PSYCHOLOGY,
William James

The full long-course, unabridged, of one of the great classics of Western literature and science. Wonderfully lucid descriptions of human mental activity, the stream of thought, consciousness, time perception, memory, imagination, emotions, reason, abnormal phenomena, and similar topics. Original contributions are integrated with the work of such men as Berkeley, Binet, Mills, Darwin, Hume, Kant, Royce, Schopenhauer, Spinoza, Locke, Descartes, Galton, Wundt, Lotze, Herbart, Fechner, and scores of others. All contrasting interpretations of mental phenomena are examined in detail—introspective analysis, philosophical interpretation, and experimental research. "A classic," *Journal of Consulting Psychology.* "The main lines are as valid as ever," *Psychoanalytical Quarterly.* "Standard reading . . . a classic of interpretation," *Psychiatric Quarterly.* 94 illustrations. 1408pp. 5⅜ x 8.

Vol. 1 Paperbound $2.50, Vol. 2 Paperbound $2.50,
The set $5.00

VISUAL ILLUSIONS: THEIR CAUSES, CHARACTERISTICS AND APPLICATIONS,
M. Luckiesh

"Seeing is deceiving," asserts the author of this introduction to virtually every type of optical illusion known. The text both describes and explains the principles involved in color illusions, figure-ground, distance illusions, etc. 100 photographs, drawings and diagrams prove how easy it is to fool the sense: circles that aren't round, parallel lines that seem to bend, stationary figures that seem to move as you stare at them — illustration after illustration strains our credulity at what we see. Fascinating book from many points of view, from applications for artists, in camouflage, etc. to the psychology of vision. New introduction by William Ittleson, Dept. of Psychology, Queens College. Index. Bibliography. xxi + 252pp. 5⅜ x 8½. Paperbound $1.50

FADS AND FALLACIES IN THE NAME OF SCIENCE,
Martin Gardner

This is the standard account of various cults, quack systems, and delusions which have masqueraded as science: hollow earth fanatics. Reich and orgone sex energy, dianetics, Atlantis, multiple moons, Forteanism, flying saucers, medical fallacies like iridiagnosis, zone therapy, etc. A new chapter has been added on Bridey Murphy, psionics, and other recent manifestations in this field. This is a fair, reasoned appraisal of eccentric theory which provides excellent inoculation against cleverly masked nonsense. "Should be read by everyone, scientist and non-scientist alike," R. T. Birge, Prof. Emeritus of Physics, Univ. of California; Former President, American Physical Society. Index. x + 365pp. 5⅜ x 8. Paperbound $1.85

ILLUSIONS AND DELUSIONS OF THE SUPERNATURAL AND THE OCCULT,
D. H. Rawcliffe

Holds up to rational examination hundreds of persistent delusions including crystal gazing, automatic writing, table turning, mediumistic trances, mental healing, stigmata, lycanthropy, live burial, the Indian Rope Trick, spiritualism, dowsing, telepathy, clairvoyance, ghosts, ESP, etc. The author explains and exposes the mental and physical deceptions involved, making this not only an exposé of supernatural phenomena, but a valuable exposition of characteristic types of abnormal psychology. Originally titled "The Psychology of the Occult." 14 illustrations. Index. 551pp. 5⅜ x 8. Paperbound $2.25

FAIRY TALE COLLECTIONS, *edited by Andrew Lang*
Andrew Lang's fairy tale collections make up the richest shelf-full of traditional children's stories anywhere available. Lang supervised the translation of stories from all over the world—familiar European tales collected by Grimm, animal stories from Negro Africa, myths of primitive Australia, stories from Russia, Hungary, Iceland, Japan, and many other countries. Lang's selection of translations are unusually high; many authorities consider that the most familiar tales find their best versions in these volumes. All collections are richly decorated and illustrated by H. J. Ford and other artists.

THE BLUE FAIRY BOOK. 37 stories. 138 illustrations. ix + 390pp. 5⅜ x 8½.
Paperbound $1.50

THE GREEN FAIRY BOOK. 42 stories. 100 illustrations. xiii + 366pp. 5⅜ x 8½.
Paperbound $1.50

THE BROWN FAIRY BOOK. 32 stories. 50 illustrations, 8 in color. xii + 350pp. 5⅜ x 8½.
Paperbound $1.50

THE BEST TALES OF HOFFMANN, *edited by E. F. Bleiler*
10 stories by E. T. A. Hoffmann, one of the greatest of all writers of fantasy. The tales include "The Golden Flower Pot," "Automata," "A New Year's Eve Adventure," "Nutcracker and the King of Mice," "Sand-Man," and others. Vigorous characterizations of highly eccentric personalities, remarkably imaginative situations, and intensely fast pacing has made these tales popular all over the world for 150 years. Editor's introduction. 7 drawings by Hoffmann. xxxiii + 419pp. 5⅜ x 8½.
Paperbound $2.00

GHOST AND HORROR STORIES OF AMBROSE BIERCE,
edited by E. F. Bleiler
Morbid, eerie, horrifying tales of possessed poets, shabby aristocrats, revived corpses, and haunted malefactors. Widely acknowledged as the best of their kind between Poe and the moderns, reflecting their author's inner torment and bitter view of life. Includes "Damned Thing," "The Middle Toe of the Right Foot," "The Eyes of the Panther," "Visions of the Night," "Moxon's Master," and over a dozen others. Editor's introduction. xxii + 199pp. 5⅜ x 8½.
Paperbound $1.25

THREE GOTHIC NOVELS, *edited by E. F. Bleiler*
Originators of the still popular Gothic novel form, influential in ushering in early 19th-century Romanticism. Horace Walpole's *Castle of Otranto*, William Beckford's *Vathek*, John Polidori's *The Vampyre*, and a *Fragment* by Lord Byron are enjoyable as exciting reading or as documents in the history of English literature. Editor's introduction. xi + 291pp. 5⅜ x 8½.
Paperbound $2.00

BEST GHOST STORIES OF LEFANU, *edited by E. F. Bleiler*
Though admired by such critics as V. S. Pritchett, Charles Dickens and Henry James, ghost stories by the Irish novelist Joseph Sheridan LeFanu have never become as widely known as his detective fiction. About half of the 16 stories in this collection have never before been available in America. Collection includes "Carmilla" (perhaps the best vampire story ever written), "The Haunted Baronet," "The Fortunes of Sir Robert Ardagh," and the classic "Green Tea." Editor's introduction. 7 contemporary illustrations. Portrait of LeFanu. xii + 467pp. 5⅜ x 8.
Paperbound $2.00

EASY-TO-DO ENTERTAINMENTS AND DIVERSIONS WITH COINS, CARDS, STRING, PAPER AND MATCHES, *R. M. Abraham*

Over 300 tricks, games and puzzles will provide young readers with absorbing fun. Sections on card games; paper-folding; tricks with coins, matches and pieces of string; games for the agile; toy-making from common household objects; mathematical recreations; and 50 miscellaneous pastimes. Anyone in charge of groups of youngsters, including hard-pressed parents, and in need of suggestions on how to keep children sensibly amused and quietly content will find this book indispensable. Clear, simple text, copious number of delightful line drawings and illustrative diagrams. Originally titled "Winter Nights' Entertainments." Introduction by Lord Baden Powell. 329 illustrations. v + 186pp. 5⅜ x 8½. Paperbound $1.00

AN INTRODUCTION TO CHESS MOVES AND TACTICS SIMPLY EXPLAINED, *Leonard Barden*

Beginner's introduction to the royal game. Names, possible moves of the pieces, definitions of essential terms, how games are won, etc. explained in 30-odd pages. With this background you'll be able to sit right down and play. Balance of book teaches strategy — openings, middle game, typical endgame play, and suggestions for improving your game. A sample game is fully analyzed. True middle-level introduction, teaching you all the essentials without oversimplifying or losing you in a maze of detail. 58 figures. 102pp. 5⅜ x 8½. Paperbound $1.00

LASKER'S MANUAL OF CHESS, *Dr. Emanuel Lasker*

Probably the greatest chess player of modern times, Dr. Emanuel Lasker held the world championship 28 years, independent of passing schools or fashions. This unmatched study of the game, chiefly for intermediate to skilled players, analyzes basic methods, combinations, position play, the aesthetics of chess, dozens of different openings, etc., with constant reference to great modern games. Contains a brilliant exposition of Steinitz's important theories. Introduction by Fred Reinfeld. Tables of Lasker's tournament record. 3 indices. 308 diagrams. 1 photograph. xxx + 349pp. 5⅜ x 8. Paperbound $2.25

COMBINATIONS: THE HEART OF CHESS, *Irving Chernev*

Step-by-step from simple combinations to complex, this book, by a well-known chess writer, shows you the intricacies of pins, counter-pins, knight forks, and smothered mates. Other chapters show alternate lines of play to those taken in actual championship games; boomerang combinations; classic examples of brilliant combination play by Nimzovich, Rubinstein, Tarrasch, Botvinnik, Alekhine and Capablanca. Index. 356 diagrams. ix + 245pp. 5⅜ x 8½. Paperbound $1.85

HOW TO SOLVE CHESS PROBLEMS, *K. S. Howard*

Full of practical suggestions for the fan or the beginner — who knows only the moves of the chessmen. Contains preliminary section and 58 two-move, 46 three-move, and 8 four-move problems composed by 27 outstanding American problem creators in the last 30 years. Explanation of all terms and exhaustive index. "Just what is wanted for the student," Brian Harley. 112 problems, solutions. vi + 171pp. 5⅜ x 8. Paperbound $1.35

SOCIAL THOUGHT FROM LORE TO SCIENCE,
H. E. Barnes and H. Becker

An immense survey of sociological thought and ways of viewing, studying, planning, and reforming society from earliest times to the present. Includes thought on society of preliterate peoples, ancient non-Western cultures, and every great movement in Europe, America, and modern Japan. Analyzes hundreds of great thinkers: Plato, Augustine, Bodin, Vico, Montesquieu, Herder, Comte, Marx, etc. Weighs the contributions of utopians, sophists, fascists and communists; economists, jurists, philosophers, ecclesiastics, and every 19th and 20th century school of scientific sociology, anthropology, and social psychology throughout the world. Combines topical, chronological, and regional approaches, treating the evolution of social thought as a process rather than as a series of mere topics. "Impressive accuracy, competence, and discrimination . . . easily the best single survey," *Nation*. Thoroughly revised, with new material up to 1960. 2 indexes. Over 2200 bibliographical notes. Three volume set. Total of 1586pp. 5⅜ x 8.
Vol. 1 Paperbound $2.75, Vol. 2 Paperbound $2.75, Vol. 3 Paperbound $2.50
The set $8.00

A HISTORY OF HISTORICAL WRITING, *Harry Elmer Barnes*

Virtually the only adequate survey of the whole course of historical writing in a single volume. Surveys developments from the beginnings of historiography in the ancient Near East and the Classical World, up through the Cold War. Covers major historians in detail, shows interrelationship with cultural background, makes clear individual contributions, evaluates and estimates importance; also enormously rich upon minor authors and thinkers who are usually passed over. Packed with scholarship and learning, clear, easily written. Indispensable to every student of history. Revised and enlarged up to 1961. Index and bibliography. xv + 442pp. 5⅜ x 8½.   Paperbound $2.50

JOHANN SEBASTIAN BACH, *Philipp Spitta*

The complete and unabridged text of the definitive study of Bach. Written some 70 years ago, it is still unsurpassed for its coverage of nearly all aspects of Bach's life and work. There could hardly be a finer non-techn¹cal introduction to Bach's music than the detailed, lucid analyses which Spitta provides for hundreds of individual pieces. 26 solid pages are devoted to the B minor mass, for example, and 30 pages to the glorious St. Matthew Passion. This monumental set also includes a major analysis of the music of the 18th century: Buxtehude, Pachelbel, etc. "Unchallenged as the last word on one of the supreme geniuses of music," John Barkham, *Saturday Review Syndicate*. Total of 1819pp. Heavy cloth binding. 5⅜ x 8.
Two volume set, clothbound $13.50

BEETHOVEN AND HIS NINE SYMPHONIES, *George Grove*

In this modern middle-level classic of musicology Grove not only analyzes all nine of Beethoven's symphonies very thoroughly in terms of their musical structure, but also discusses the circumstances under which they were written, Beethoven's stylistic development, and much other background material. This is an extremely rich book, yet very easily followed; it is highly recommended to anyone seriously interested in music. Over 250 musical passages. Index. viii + 407pp. 5⅜ x 8.   Paperbound $2.00

EASY-TO-DO ENTERTAINMENTS AND DIVERSIONS WITH COINS, CARDS, STRING, PAPER AND MATCHES, *R. M. Abraham*
Over 300 tricks, games and puzzles will provide young readers with absorbing fun. Sections on card games; paper-folding; tricks with coins, matches and pieces of string; games for the agile; toy-making from common household objects; mathematical recreations; and 50 miscellaneous pastimes. Anyone in charge of groups of youngsters, including hard-pressed parents, and in need of suggestions on how to keep children sensibly amused and quietly content will find this book indispensable. Clear, simple text, copious number of delightful line drawings and illustrative diagrams. Originally titled "Winter Nights' Entertainments." Introduction by Lord Baden Powell. 329 illustrations. v + 186pp. 5⅜ x 8½. Paperbound $1.00

AN INTRODUCTION TO CHESS MOVES AND TACTICS SIMPLY EXPLAINED, *Leonard Barden*
Beginner's introduction to the royal game. Names, possible moves of the pieces, definitions of essential terms, how games are won, etc. explained in 30-odd pages. With this background you'll be able to sit right down and play. Balance of book teaches strategy — openings, middle game, typical endgame play, and suggestions for improving your game. A sample game is fully analyzed. True middle-level introduction, teaching you all the essentials without oversimplifying or losing you in a maze of detail. 58 figures. 102pp. 5⅜ x 8½. Paperbound $1.00

LASKER'S MANUAL OF CHESS, *Dr. Emanuel Lasker*
Probably the greatest chess player of modern times, Dr. Emanuel Lasker held the world championship 28 years, independent of passing schools or fashions. This unmatched study of the game, chiefly for intermediate to skilled players, analyzes basic methods, combinations, position play, the aesthetics of chess, dozens of different openings, etc., with constant reference to great modern games. Contains a brilliant exposition of Steinitz's important theories. Introduction by Fred Reinfeld. Tables of Lasker's tournament record. 3 indices. 308 diagrams. 1 photograph. xxx + 349pp. 5⅜ x 8. Paperbound $2.25

COMBINATIONS: THE HEART OF CHESS, *Irving Chernev*
Step-by-step from simple combinations to complex, this book, by a well-known chess writer, shows you the intricacies of pins, counter-pins, knight forks, and smothered mates. Other chapters show alternate lines of play to those taken in actual championship games; boomerang combinations; classic examples of brilliant combination play by Nimzovich, Rubinstein, Tarrasch, Botvinnik, Alekhine and Capablanca. Index. 356 diagrams. ix + 245pp. 5⅜ x 8½. Paperbound $1.85

HOW TO SOLVE CHESS PROBLEMS, *K. S. Howard*
Full of practical suggestions for the fan or the beginner — who knows only the moves of the chessmen. Contains preliminary section and 58 two-move, 46 three-move, and 8 four-move problems composed by 27 outstanding American problem creators in the last 30 years. Explanation of all terms and exhaustive index. "Just what is wanted for the student," Brian Harley. 112 problems, solutions. vi + 171pp. 5⅜ x 8. Paperbound $1.35

SOCIAL THOUGHT FROM LORE TO SCIENCE,
H. E. Barnes and H. Becker
An immense survey of sociological thought and ways of viewing, studying, planning, and reforming society from earliest times to the present. Includes thought on society of preliterate peoples, ancient non-Western cultures, and every great movement in Europe, America, and modern Japan. Analyzes hundreds of great thinkers: Plato, Augustine, Bodin, Vico, Montesquieu, Herder, Comte, Marx, etc. Weighs the contributions of utopians, sophists, fascists and communists; economists, jurists, philosophers, ecclesiastics, and every 19th and 20th century school of scientific sociology, anthropology, and social psychology throughout the world. Combines topical, chronological, and regional approaches, treating the evolution of social thought as a process rather than as a series of mere topics. "Impressive accuracy, competence, and discrimination . . . easily the best single survey," *Nation*. Thoroughly revised, with new material up to 1960. 2 indexes. Over 2200 bibliographical notes. Three volume set. Total of 1586pp. 5⅜ x 8.
Vol. 1 Paperbound $2.75, Vol. 2 Paperbound $2.75, Vol. 3 Paperbound $2.50
The set $8.00

A HISTORY OF HISTORICAL WRITING, *Harry Elmer Barnes*
Virtually the only adequate survey of the whole course of historical writing in a single volume. Surveys developments from the beginnings of historiography in the ancient Near East and the Classical World, up through the Cold War. Covers major historians in detail, shows interrelationship with cultural background, makes clear individual contributions, evaluates and estimates importance; also enormously rich upon minor authors and thinkers who are usually passed over. Packed with scholarship and learning, clear, easily written. Indispensable to every student of history. Revised and enlarged up to 1961. Index and bibliography. xv + 442pp. 5⅜ x 8½.   Paperbound $2.50

JOHANN SEBASTIAN BACH, *Philipp Spitta*
The complete and unabridged text of the definitive study of Bach. Written some 70 years ago, it is still unsurpassed for its coverage of nearly all aspects of Bach's life and work. There could hardly be a finer non-techn'cal introduction to Bach's music than the detailed, lucid analyses which Spitta provides for hundreds of individual pieces. 26 solid pages are devoted to the B minor mass, for example, and 30 pages to the glorious St. Matthew Passion. This monumental set also includes a major analysis of the music of the 18th century: Buxtehude, Pachelbel, etc. "Unchallenged as the last word on one of the supreme geniuses of music," John Barkham, *Saturday Review Syndicate*. Total of 1819pp. Heavy cloth binding. 5⅜ x 8.
Two volume set, clothbound $13.50

BEETHOVEN AND HIS NINE SYMPHONIES, *George Grove*
In this modern middle-level classic of musicology Grove not only analyzes all nine of Beethoven's symphonies very thoroughly in terms of their musical structure, but also discusses the circumstances under which they were written, Beethoven's stylistic development, and much other background material. This is an extremely rich book, yet very easily followed; it is highly recommended to anyone seriously interested in music. Over 250 musical passages. Index. viii + 407pp. 5⅜ x 8.
Paperbound $2.00

THREE SCIENCE FICTION NOVELS,
John Taine
Acknowledged by many as the best SF writer of the 1920's, Taine (under the name Eric Temple Bell) was also a Professor of Mathematics of considerable renown. Reprinted here are *The Time Stream*, generally considered Taine's best, *The Greatest Game*, a biological-fiction novel, and *The Purple Sapphire*, involving a supercivilization of the past. Taine's stories tie fantastic narratives to frameworks of original and logical scientific concepts. Speculation is often profound on such questions as the nature of time, concept of entropy, cyclical universes, etc. 4 contemporary illustrations. v + 532pp. 5⅜ x 8⅜.
Paperbound $2.00

SEVEN SCIENCE FICTION NOVELS,
H. G. Wells
Full unabridged texts of 7 science-fiction novels of the master. Ranging from biology, physics, chemistry, astronomy, to sociology and other studies, Mr. Wells extrapolates whole worlds of strange and intriguing character. "One will have to go far to match this for entertainment, excitement, and sheer pleasure . . ."*New York Times*. Contents: The Time Machine, The Island of Dr. Moreau, The First Men in the Moon, The Invisible Man, The War of the Worlds, The Food of the Gods, In The Days of the Comet. 1015pp. 5⅜ x 8.
Clothbound $5.00

28 SCIENCE FICTION STORIES OF H. G. WELLS.
Two full, unabridged novels, *Men Like Gods* and *Star Begotten*, plus 26 short stories by the master science-fiction writer of all time! Stories of space, time, invention, exploration, futuristic adventure. Partial contents: *The Country of the Blind, In the Abyss, The Crystal Egg, The Man Who Could Work Miracles, A Story of Days to Come, The Empire of the Ants, The Magic Shop, The Valley of the Spiders, A Story of the Stone Age, Under the Knife, Sea Raiders,* etc. An indispensable collection for the library of anyone interested in science fiction adventure. 928pp. 5⅜ x 8.
Clothbound $4.50

THREE MARTIAN NOVELS,
Edgar Rice Burroughs
Complete, unabridged reprinting, in one volume, of Thuvia, Maid of Mars; Chessmen of Mars; The Master Mind of Mars. Hours of science-fiction adventure by a modern master storyteller. Reset in large clear type for easy reading. 16 illustrations by J. Allen St. John. vi + 490pp. 5⅜ x 8½.
Paperbound $1.85

AN INTELLECTUAL AND CULTURAL HISTORY OF THE WESTERN WORLD,
Harry Elmer Barnes
Monumental 3-volume survey of intellectual development of Europe from primitive cultures to the present day. Every significant product of human intellect traced through history: art, literature, mathematics, physical sciences, medicine, music, technology, social sciences, religions, jurisprudence, education, etc. Presentation is lucid and specific, analyzing in detail specific discoveries, theories, literary works, and so on. Revised (1965) by recognized scholars in specialized fields under the direction of Prof. Barnes. Revised bibliography. Indexes. 24 illustrations. Total of xxix + 1318pp.
Vol. 1 Paperbound $2.00, Vol. 2 Paperbound $2.00, Vol. 3 Paperbound $2.00,
The set $6.00

HEAR ME TALKIN' TO YA, *edited by Nat Shapiro and Nat Hentoff*
In their own words, Louis Armstrong, King Oliver, Fletcher Henderson, Bunk Johnson, Bix Beiderbecke, Billy Holiday, Fats Waller, Jelly Roll Morton, Duke Ellington, and many others comment on the origins of jazz in New Orleans and its growth in Chicago's South Side, Kansas City's jam sessions, Depression Harlem, and the modernism of the West Coast schools. Taken from taped conversations, letters, magazine articles, other first-hand sources. Editors' introduction. xvi + 429pp. 5⅜ x 8½.   Paperbound $2.00

THE JOURNAL OF HENRY D. THOREAU
A 25-year record by the great American observer and critic, as complete a record of a great man's inner life as is anywhere available. Thoreau's Journals served him as raw material for his formal pieces, as a place where he could develop his ideas, as an outlet for his interests in wild life and plants, in writing as an art, in classics of literature, Walt Whitman and other contemporaries, in politics, slavery, individual's relation to the State, etc. The Journals present a portrait of a remarkable man, and are an observant social history. Unabridged republication of 1906 edition, Bradford Torrey and Francis H. Allen, editors. Illustrations. Total of 1888pp. 8⅜ x 12¼.
          Two volume set, clothbound $25.00

A SHAKESPEARIAN GRAMMAR, *E. A. Abbott*
Basic reference to Shakespeare and his contemporaries, explaining through thousands of quotations from Shakespeare, Jonson, Beaumont and Fletcher, North's *Plutarch* and other sources the grammatical usage differing from the modern. First published in 1870 and written by a scholar who spent much of his life isolating principles of Elizabethan language, the book is unlikely ever to be superseded. Indexes. xxiv + 511pp. 5⅜ x 8½.   Paperbound $2.75

FOLK-LORE OF SHAKESPEARE, *T. F. Thistelton Dyer*
Classic study, drawing from Shakespeare a large body of references to supernatural beliefs, terminology of falconry and hunting, games and sports, good luck charms, marriage customs, folk medicines, superstitions about plants, animals, birds, argot of the underworld, sexual slang of London, proverbs, drinking customs, weather lore, and much else. From full compilation comes a mirror of the 17th-century popular mind. Index. ix + 526pp. 5⅜ x 8½.
          Paperbound $2.50

THE NEW VARIORUM SHAKESPEARE, *edited by H. H. Furness*
By far the richest editions of the plays ever produced in any country or language. Each volume contains complete text (usually First Folio) of the play, all variants in Quarto and other Folio texts, editorial changes by every major editor to Furness's own time (1900), footnotes to obscure references or language, extensive quotes from literature of Shakespearian criticism, essays on plot sources (often reprinting sources in full), and much more.

HAMLET, *edited by H. H. Furness*
Total of xxvi + 905pp. 5⅜ x 8½.   Two volume set, paperbound $4.75

TWELFTH NIGHT, *edited by H. H. Furness*
Index. xxii + 434pp. 5⅜ x 8½.   Paperbound $2.25

LA BOHEME BY GIACOMO PUCCINI,
translated and introduced by Ellen H. Bleiler
Complete handbook for the operagoer, with everything needed for full enjoyment except the musical score itself. Complete Italian libretto, with new, modern English line-by-line translation—the only libretto printing all repeats; biography of Puccini; the librettists; background to the opera, Murger's La Boheme, etc.; circumstances of composition and performances; plot summary; and pictorial section of 73 illustrations showing Puccini, famous singers and performances, etc. Large clear type for easy reading. 124pp. 5⅜ x 8½.
Paperbound $1.00

ANTONIO STRADIVARI: HIS LIFE AND WORK (1644-1737),
W. Henry Hill, Arthur F. Hill, and Alfred E. Hill
Still the only book that really delves into life and art of the incomparable Italian craftsman, maker of the finest musical instruments in the world today. The authors, expert violin-makers themselves, discuss Stradivari's ancestry, his construction and finishing techniques, distinguished characteristics of many of his instruments and their locations. Included, too, is story of introduction of his instruments into France, England, first revelation of their supreme merit, and information on his labels, number of instruments made, prices, mystery of ingredients of his varnish, tone of pre-1684 Stradivari violin and changes between 1684 and 1690. An extremely interesting, informative account for all music lovers, from craftsman to concert-goer. Republication of original (1902) edition. New introduction by Sydney Beck, Head of Rare Book and Manuscript Collections, Music Division, New York Public Library. Analytical index by Rembert Wurlitzer. Appendixes. 68 illustrations. 30 full-page plates. 4 in color. xxvi + 315pp. 5⅜ x 8½. Paperbound $2.25

MUSICAL AUTOGRAPHS FROM MONTEVERDI TO HINDEMITH,
Emanuel Winternitz
For beauty, for intrinsic interest, for perspective on the composer's personality, for subtleties of phrasing, shading, emphasis indicated in the autograph but suppressed in the printed score, the mss. of musical composition are fascinating documents which repay close study in many different ways. This 2-volume work reprints facsimiles of mss. by virtually every major composer, and many minor figures—196 examples in all. A full text points out what can be learned from mss., analyzes each sample. Index. Bibliography. 18 figures. 196 plates. Total of 170pp. of text. 7⅞ x 10¾.
Vol. 1 Paperbound $2.00, Vol. 2 Paperbound $2.00,
The set $4.00

J. S. BACH,
Albert Schweitzer
One of the few great full-length studies of Bach's life and work, and the study upon which Schweitzer's renown as a musicologist rests. On first appearance (1911), revolutionized Bach performance. The only writer on Bach to be musicologist, performing musician, and student of history, theology and philosophy, Schweitzer contributes particularly full sections on history of German Protestant church music, theories on motivic pictorial representations in vocal music, and practical suggestions for performance. Translated by Ernest Newman. Indexes. 5 illustrations. 650 musical examples. Total of xix + 928pp. 5⅜ x 8½. Vol. 1 Paperbound $2.00, Vol. 2 Paperbound $2.00,
The set $4.00

THE METHODS OF ETHICS, *Henry Sidgwick*
Propounding no organized system of its own, study subjects every major
methodological approach to ethics to rigorous, objective analysis. Study discusses and relates ethical thought of Plato, Aristotle, Bentham, Clarke, Butler,
Hobbes, Hume, Mill, Spencer, Kant, and dozens of others. Sidgwick retains
conclusions from each system which follow from ethical premises, rejecting
the faulty. Considered by many in the field to be among the most important
treatises on ethical philosophy. Appendix. Index. xlvii + 528pp. 5⅜ x 8½.
Paperbound $2.50

TEUTONIC MYTHOLOGY, *Jakob Grimm*
A milestone in Western culture; the work which established on a modern
basis the study of history of religions and comparative religions. 4-volume
work assembles and interprets everything available on religious and folk-
loristic beliefs of Germanic people (including Scandinavians, Anglo-Saxons,
etc.). Assembling material from such sources as Tacitus, surviving Old Norse
and Icelandic texts, archeological remains, folktales, surviving superstitions,
comparative traditions, linguistic analysis, etc. Grimm explores pagan deities,
heroes, folklore of nature, religious practices, and every other area of pagan
German belief. To this day, the unrivaled, definitive, exhaustive study. Translated by J. S. Stallybrass from 4th (1883) German edition. Indexes. Total of
lxxvii + 1887pp. 5⅜ x 8½.   Four volume set, paperbound $10.00

THE I CHING, *translated by James Legge*
Called "The Book of Changes" in English, this is one of the Five Classics
edited by Confucius, basic and central to Chinese thought. Explains perhaps
the most complex system of divination known, founded on the theory that all
things happening at any one time have characteristic features which can be
isolated and related. Significant in Oriental studies, in history of religions and
philosophy, and also to Jungian psychoanalysis and other areas of modern
European thought. Index. Appendixes. 6 plates. xxi + 448pp. 5⅜ x 8½.
Paperbound $2.75

HISTORY OF ANCIENT PHILOSOPHY, *W. Windelband*
One of the clearest, most accurate comprehensive surveys of Greek and Roman
philosophy. Discusses ancient philosophy in general, intellectual life in Greece
in the 7th and 6th centuries B.C., Thales, Anaximander, Anaximenes, Herac-
litus, the Eleatics, Empedocles, Anaxagoras, Leucippus, the Pythagoreans, the
Sophists, Socrates, Democritus (20 pages), Plato (50 pages), Aristotle (70 pages),
the Peripatetics, Stoics, Epicureans, Sceptics, Neo-platonists, Christian Apolo-
gists, etc. 2nd German edition translated by H. E. Cushman. xv + 393pp.
5⅜ x 8.   Paperbound $2.25

THE PALACE OF PLEASURE, *William Painter*
Elizabethan versions of Italian and French novels from *The Decameron*,
Cinthio, Straparola, Queen Margaret of Navarre, and other continental sources
— the very work that provided Shakespeare and dozens of his contemporaries
with many of their plots and sub-plots and, therefore, justly considered one of
the most influential books in all English literature. It is also a book that any
reader will still enjoy. Total of cviii + 1,224pp.
Three volume set, Paperbound $6.75

THREE SCIENCE FICTION NOVELS,
John Taine
Acknowledged by many as the best SF writer of the 1920's, Taine (under the name Eric Temple Bell) was also a Professor of Mathematics of considerable renown. Reprinted here are *The Time Stream*, generally considered Taine's best, *The Greatest Game*, a biological-fiction novel, and *The Purple Sapphire*, involving a supercivilization of the past. Taine's stories tie fantastic narratives to frameworks of original and logical scientific concepts. Speculation is often profound on such questions as the nature of time, concept of entropy, cyclical universes, etc. 4 contemporary illustrations. v + 532pp. 5⅜ x 8⅜.
Paperbound $2.00

SEVEN SCIENCE FICTION NOVELS,
H. G. Wells
Full unabridged texts of 7 science-fiction novels of the master. Ranging from biology, physics, chemistry, astronomy, to sociology and other studies, Mr. Wells extrapolates whole worlds of strange and intriguing character. "One will have to go far to match this for entertainment, excitement, and sheer pleasure . . ."*New York Times.* Contents: The Time Machine, The Island of Dr. Moreau, The First Men in the Moon, The Invisible Man, The War of the Worlds, The Food of the Gods, In The Days of the Comet. 1015pp. 5⅜ x 8.
Clothbound $5.00

28 SCIENCE FICTION STORIES OF H. G. WELLS.
Two full, unabridged novels, *Men Like Gods* and *Star Begotten*, plus 26 short stories by the master science-fiction writer of all time! Stories of space, time, invention, exploration, futuristic adventure. Partial contents: *The Country of the Blind, In the Abyss, The Crystal Egg, The Man Who Could Work Miracles, A Story of Days to Come, The Empire of the Ants, The Magic Shop, The Valley of the Spiders, A Story of the Stone Age, Under the Knife, Sea Raiders,* etc. An indispensable collection for the library of anyone interested in science fiction adventure. 928pp. 5⅜ x 8.
Clothbound $4.50

THREE MARTIAN NOVELS,
Edgar Rice Burroughs
Complete, unabridged reprinting, in one volume, of Thuvia, Maid of Mars; Chessmen of Mars; The Master Mind of Mars. Hours of science-fiction adventure by a modern master storyteller. Reset in large clear type for easy reading. 16 illustrations by J. Allen St. John. vi + 490pp. 5⅜ x 8½.
Paperbound $1.85

AN INTELLECTUAL AND CULTURAL HISTORY OF THE WESTERN WORLD,
Harry Elmer Barnes
Monumental 3-volume survey of intellectual development of Europe from primitive cultures to the present day. Every significant product of human intellect traced through history: art, literature, mathematics, physical sciences, medicine, music, technology, social sciences, religions, jurisprudence, education, etc. Presentation is lucid and specific, analyzing in detail specific discoveries, theories, literary works, and so on. Revised (1965) by recognized scholars in specialized fields under the direction of Prof. Barnes. Revised bibliography. Indexes. 24 illustrations. Total of xxix + 1318pp.
Vol. 1 Paperbound $2.00, Vol. 2 Paperbound $2.00, Vol. 3 Paperbound $2.00,
The set $6.00

HEAR ME TALKIN' TO YA, *edited by Nat Shapiro and Nat Hentoff*
In their own words, Louis Armstrong, King Oliver, Fletcher Henderson, Bunk Johnson, Bix Beiderbecke, Billy Holiday, Fats Waller, Jelly Roll Morton, Duke Ellington, and many others comment on the origins of jazz in New Orleans and its growth in Chicago's South Side, Kansas City's jam sessions, Depression Harlem, and the modernism of the West Coast schools. Taken from taped conversations, letters, magazine articles, other first-hand sources. Editors' introduction. xvi + 429pp. 5⅜ x 8½.   Paperbound $2.00

THE JOURNAL OF HENRY D. THOREAU
A 25-year record by the great American observer and critic, as complete a record of a great man's inner life as is anywhere available. Thoreau's Journals served him as raw material for his formal pieces, as a place where he could develop his ideas, as an outlet for his interests in wild life and plants, in writing as an art, in classics of literature, Walt Whitman and other contemporaries, in politics, slavery, individual's relation to the State, etc. The Journals present a portrait of a remarkable man, and are an observant social history. Unabridged republication of 1906 edition, Bradford Torrey and Francis H. Allen, editors. Illustrations. Total of 1888pp. 8⅜ x 12¼.
Two volume set, clothbound $25.00

A SHAKESPEARIAN GRAMMAR, *E. A. Abbott*
Basic reference to Shakespeare and his contemporaries, explaining through thousands of quotations from Shakespeare, Jonson, Beaumont and Fletcher, North's *Plutarch* and other sources the grammatical usage differing from the modern. First published in 1870 and written by a scholar who spent much of his life isolating principles of Elizabethan language, the book is unlikely ever to be superseded. Indexes. xxiv + 511pp. 5⅜ x 8½.   Paperbound $2.75

FOLK-LORE OF SHAKESPEARE, *T. F. Thistelton Dyer*
Classic study, drawing from Shakespeare a large body of references to supernatural beliefs, terminology of falconry and hunting, games and sports, good luck charms, marriage customs, folk medicines, superstitions about plants, animals, birds, argot of the underworld, sexual slang of London, proverbs, drinking customs, weather lore, and much else. From full compilation comes a mirror of the 17th-century popular mind. Index. ix + 526pp. 5⅜ x 8½.
Paperbound $2.50

THE NEW VARIORUM SHAKESPEARE, *edited by H. H. Furness*
By far the richest editions of the plays ever produced in any country or language. Each volume contains complete text (usually First Folio) of the play, all variants in Quarto and other Folio texts, editorial changes by every major editor to Furness's own time (1900), footnotes to obscure references or language, extensive quotes from literature of Shakespearian criticism, essays on plot sources (often reprinting sources in full), and much more.

HAMLET, *edited by H. H. Furness*
Total of xxvi + 905pp. 5⅜ x 8½.   Two volume set, paperbound $4.75

TWELFTH NIGHT, *edited by H. H. Furness*
Index. xxii + 434pp. 5⅜ x 8½.
Paperbound $2.25

THE WONDERFUL WIZARD OF OZ, *L. F. Baum*
All the original W. W. Denslow illustrations in full color—as much a part of "The Wizard" as Tenniel's drawings are of "Alice in Wonderland." "The Wizard" is still America's best-loved fairy tale, in which, as the author expresses it, "The wonderment and joy are retained and the heartaches and nightmares left out." Now today's young readers can enjoy every word and wonderful picture of the original book. New introduction by Martin Gardner. A Baum bibliography. 23 full-page color plates. viii + 268pp. 5⅜ x 8.
Paperbound $1.50

THE MARVELOUS LAND OF OZ, *L. F. Baum*
This is the equally enchanting sequel to the "Wizard," continuing the adventures of the Scarecrow and the Tin Woodman. The hero this time is a little boy named Tip, and all the delightful Oz magic is still present. This is the Oz book with the Animated Saw-Horse, the Woggle-Bug, and Jack Pumpkinhead. All the original John R. Neill illustrations, 10 in full color. 287pp. 5⅜ x 8.
Paperbound $1.50

ALICE'S ADVENTURES UNDER GROUND, *Lewis Carroll*
The original *Alice in Wonderland*, hand-lettered and illustrated by Carroll himself, and originally presented as a Christmas gift to a child-friend. Adults as well as children will enjoy this charming volume, reproduced faithfully in this Dover edition. While the story is essentially the same, there are slight changes, and Carroll's spritely drawings present an intriguing alternative to the famous Tenniel illustrations. One of the most popular books in Dover's catalogue. Introduction by Martin Gardner. 38 illustrations. 128pp. 5⅜ x 8½.
Paperbound $1.00

THE NURSERY "ALICE," *Lewis Carroll*
While most of us consider *Alice in Wonderland* a story for children of all ages, Carroll himself felt it was beyond younger children. He therefore provided this simplified version, illustrated with the famous Tenniel drawings enlarged and colored in delicate tints, for children aged "from Nought to Five." Dover's edition of this now rare classic is a faithful copy of the 1889 printing, including 20 illustrations by Tenniel, and front and back covers reproduced in full color. Introduction by Martin Gardner. xxiii + 67pp. 6⅛ x 9¼.
Paperbound $1.50

THE STORY OF KING ARTHUR AND HIS KNIGHTS, *Howard Pyle*
A fast-paced, exciting retelling of the best known Arthurian legends for young readers by one of America's best story tellers and illustrators. The sword Excalibur, wooing of Guinevere, Merlin and his downfall, adventures of Sir Pellias and Gawaine, and others. The pen and ink illustrations are vividly imagined and wonderfully drawn. 41 illustrations. xviii + 313pp. 6⅛ x 9¼.
Paperbound $1.50

Prices subject to change without notice.

Available at your book dealer or write for free catalogue to Dept. Adsci, Dover Publications, Inc., 180 Varick St., N.Y., N.Y. 10014. Dover publishes more than 150 books each year on science, elementary and advanced mathematics, biology, music, art, literary history, social sciences and other areas.